# LOSE IT
# *now*
# COOKBOOK

### More Than **80 SIMPLE, DELICIOUS RECIPES** for FAST WEIGHT LOSS

RODALE.

© 2016 by Rodale Inc.

Photographs © 2016 by Rodale Inc., excluding pages 27, 104 & 109

Printed in the United States of America
Rodale Inc. makes every effort to use acid-free ∞, recycled paper ♲.

Photographs by Mitch Mandel/Rodale Images, except: Jim Franco (page 27),
Marcus Nilsson (page 104), and Alexandra Rowley (page 109)
Book design by Christina Gaugler

Library of Congress Cataloging-in-Publication Data is on file with the publisher.

ISBN 978–1–62336–784–8 direct mail paperback

2   4   6   8   10   9   7   5   3   1   direct mail paperback

We inspire and enable people to improve their lives and the world around them.
rodalestore.com

# CONTENTS

# INTRODUCTION

*A*re you looking for a reliable way to lose weight and keep it off without the uncomfortable distraction of constant hunger or the obligation to count calories or grams of fat? You may be surprised to learn that goal is easier to achieve than previously thought.

As you'll learn in *Lose It Now, Lose It Forever*, there is a revolutionary new approach to weight loss that isn't about eating less food or eating less fat. Rather, when you follow the Lose It Now, Lose It Forever Program, you'll discover firsthand how lowering your insulin level is the key to successful, long-term weight loss.

Insulin is an important hormone that plays a critical function in fat metabolism. When you lower your body's insulin level, you allow your body to burn rather than store fat. Perhaps even more importantly, when you are in control of your insulin levels you are also in a better position to successfully manage the inevitable weight-loss plateau that arrives after about 4 months of steady weight loss.

All the details about this remarkable new approach to losing weight are in *Lose It Now, Lose It Forever*, but this companion cookbook was created so you can start your weight-loss journey with a solid range of delicious, easy-to-prepare, and satisfying dishes.

Craving a warm bowl of soup to take away an afternoon chill? Perhaps the Creamy Broccoli Soup on page 23 would work well. Its smooth, rich texture is drawn from silken tofu (instead of cream) to keep your insulin levels low. Need an easily portable salad for an on-the-go lunch? You'll find 16 salad recipes that are sure to keep you satisfied. In addition, you'll find close to 40 entrées and more than 30 color photographs to whet your appetite, ranging from a simple one-pan chicken dish that's ready in 20 minutes or less to a stuffed lamb chop that is sure to impress for the holidays or any special occasion.

All of the recipes in this exclusive collection are designed for you to use during the Active Phase of the Lose It Now, Lose It Forever Program. After about

4 months, when your body has reached your natural weight-loss plateau, you can still use these recipes. However, you'll want to carefully follow the steps outlined on page 134 of the companion title to see how to start slowly incorporating just the right amount of carbohydrates into your day so that you safely maintain your weight loss during the Passive Phase of the program. Remember, this step is critical if you want to be able to lose more weight in the future.

But before you race to the kitchen and start making a grocery list for yourself, it's a good idea to take a few minutes and review a few key elements of this program so that you'll have a better understanding of what to expect and what makes *Lose It Now, Lose It Forever* so truly valuable.

## WHY THIS PROGRAM WON'T LEAVE YOU FEELING HUNGRY

If you've followed restrictive diets in the past, you may have lowered your caloric intake to the point where your stomach was growling like an angry beast several times a day. As a result, perhaps you then guzzled a few extra bottles of water, hoping that would make you feel full. Assuming the cravings were kept at bay, did you later reward yourself and then feel guilty? Were you tempted to punish yourself afterward? If this scenario sounds familiar, you've experienced a common no-win cycle that rarely leads to long-term weight loss for anyone.

The Lose It Now, Lose It Forever Program is not a diet for this very reason. This program was designed to help you break this endless and frustrating loop by changing your thinking. Instead of evaluating your food choices in terms of calories or fat grams, you'll have the information you need to understand how different foods will affect your insulin levels. While it is true that reducing your caloric intake will help you lose weight, when you lower your insulin level you'll lose weight by burning fat. As an added bonus, you'll also have much better control over your cravings.

Along the same lines, it is important to remember that the goal with this program is to enjoy satisfying meals, not to leave the table feeling hungry. Most recipes in this cookbook are written to make 4 servings, but this is simply a guideline. The reality is that as long as you are enjoying foods that keep your insulin under control, you should eat as much as you need. Fortunately, if you follow the 7-day menu plan that begins on page 138, you will be just fine. You will eat well five times a day. For lunch and dinner, you will have at least a portion of proteins and a portion of green, leafy vegetables. And you can have more, if necessary, to feel satisfied and full.

## WHAT SHOULD YOU EAT?

The recipes in this cookbook make it easy to get off to a good start with the Lose It Now, Lose It Forever Program. However, occasions will inevitably arise when you need to make some decisions on your own. Whenever you're faced with food choices, simply categorize your options into five groups—sweets, fruits, grains, vegetables, or proteins.

When food choices fall into the sweets and grains category, steer clear: These are foods that will spike your insulin level, so avoid eating them. Once you've identified foods as either vegetables or fruits, just remember that you can eat all vegetables except for four—potatoes, corn, carrots, and beets. On the other hand, you can eat only four fruits—apples, oranges, grapes, or berries—and no others. You can have all proteins, such as meat, seafood, chicken, or egg whites, because they barely spike insulin. It's that simple!

## WHAT SHOULD YOU DRINK?

When following the Lose It Now, Lose It Forever Program, it's best to avoid any drinks that are sweet. That includes those sweetened with artificial sweeteners. What can you drink, then, that won't spike your insulin level? Water is fine. What if you're tired of drinking plain water? You may consider adding lemon, lime, cucumber, or fresh mint to water. How about unsweetened iced tea or hot tea? Sure! Tea has thousands of varieties to taste. The same goes for coffee. As long as you're not adding anything sweet, such as agave, honey, sugar, or artificial sweeteners, that would be fine.

Here's to a successful weight-loss journey and many wonderful meals along the way. Cheers!

# BREAKFASTS

# Very Berry Smoothie (right)

*Smoothies take less than 5 minutes to make and can taste like a five-star dessert. What's not to love about that? If you prefer your smoothies to be extra-light and frothy, add more ice.*

1 cup 0% plain Greek yogurt

¾ cup fat-free milk

1 cup mixed frozen blueberries, strawberries, and raspberries

3 ice cubes, crushed

In a blender, combine the yogurt, milk, berries, and ice. Blend until smooth.

**Serves: 1 • Prep Time: 5 MINUTES • Total Time: 5 MINUTES**

# Ricotta Pudding

*The thin, brightly colored portion of a citrus peel, often called the zest, is rich in essential oils that can bring a bright, fresh flavor to dishes. To zest the fruit, place a fine grater or rasp over a plate and pull it to release the peel. Be sure to remove only the colored portion, as the white membrane is quite bitter. This recipe is great when you plan to eat an orange for your morning snack. Zest it for breakfast but don't peel the orange until just before eating.*

½ cup part-skim ricotta cheese

Pinch of pure stevia

¾ cup 0% plain Greek yogurt

½ teaspoon grated orange peel

1. In a food processor or blender, puree the ricotta and stevia until smooth. Scrape into a medium bowl.

2. Stir in the yogurt and orange peel.

**Serves: 2 • Prep Time: 5 MINUTES • Total Time: 5 MINUTES**

# INGREDIENT GUIDE: *Berries*

**TO SELECT THE BEST BERRIES,** look for:

- A heady perfume
- A box without excessive stains on the bottom
- Locally grown berries when possible

**TO STORE,** gently spill the berries onto a paper towel. Remove any that are mushy or show signs of mold. Spread the rest in a single layer on a plate or a small baking sheet lined with paper towels. Cover with another layer of paper towels and refrigerate until ready to use.

**TO WASH,** wait to wash berries until just before using. This helps prevent mushy berries. Rinse them gently with cool water and then pat dry with paper towels. To keep strawberries from getting soggy, leave the hulls intact until after washing. The hulls work as a cork and keep the berries from absorbing water.

**TO FREEZE,** wash the berries and pat dry, then spread them on a waxed paper–lined baking sheet, making sure that they don't touch. Freeze for several hours until solid, then loosen from the paper, using a spatula if necessary. Transfer the berries to a zip-top freezer bag and freeze for up to 9 months. This freezing method prevents the berries from freezing together and allows you to remove just the amount needed from the bag.

**TO REMOVE BERRY STAINS,** rub them with a wedge of lemon.

**DID YOU KNOW?** Blueberries are one of the top sources of antioxidants found in the produce aisle. Antioxidants fight free radicals, helping to prevent cancer, high blood cholesterol, and aging skin. Genetically from the same plant family as cranberries, blueberries and their juice also contain condensed tannins, which help fight urinary tract infections. Technically, a huge range of fruits falls under the berry category, but for our purposes we'll concentrate on strawberries, blueberries, and raspberries.

---

**FASCINATING FACT:** *Each raspberry and blackberry has a delicate cluster of 75 to 125 plump, juice-filled drupelets, each of which holds a berry seed.*

# Broccoli-Cheddar Scramble

*This quick breakfast for one is easily multiplied. Simply double the recipe and use a large skillet instead.*

1 teaspoon olive oil

½ cup chopped broccoli

½ cup chopped mushrooms

⅓ cup chopped red or green bell peppers

¾ cup egg whites

¼ cup shredded reduced-fat Cheddar cheese

1. In a small nonstick skillet over medium-high heat, warm the oil. Cook the broccoli, mushrooms, and peppers, stirring frequently, for 5 minutes, or until tender.

2. Reduce the heat to medium-low and add the egg whites. As the mixture begins to set on the bottom of the pan, scrape it up with a spatula until all the egg is set.

3. Remove from the heat and scatter the cheese on top. Cover the skillet for a few minutes until the cheese is melted.

**Serves: 1 • Prep Time: 5 MINUTES • Total Time: 15 MINUTES**

# Deviled Eggs

*Hard-cooked eggs are readily available in most groceries, so these delicious eggs are a snap to prepare. If you choose to cook your own, place the eggs in a single layer in a pan filled with enough water to cover them by 1". Bring the water to a boil over high heat and immediately remove from the heat as soon as the water begins to boil. Let the eggs sit, covered, for exactly 15 minutes. Drain and rinse the eggs under cold running water until cool enough to peel.*

6 large hard-cooked eggs, shelled and halved lengthwise

¼ cup 1% plain Greek yogurt

2 teaspoons Dijon mustard

¼ teaspoon salt

¼ teaspoon paprika

½ teaspoon chopped chives (optional)

In a medium bowl, combine the egg yolks, yogurt, mustard, salt, and paprika. With a fork, mash until well blended. Place the egg white halves on a plate, hollow side up. Dollop the yolk mixture into the egg whites. Scatter with the chives, if desired.

**Serves: 6 • Prep Time: 10 MINUTES • Total Time: 10 MINUTES**

# Scrambled Eggs and Shrimp

*It's a good idea to keep some frozen baby shrimp on hand for quick meals. Here they're mixed into scrambled eggs for a no-fuss brunch dish.*

6 large egg whites

2 large eggs

1 tablespoon water

1 teaspoon hot-pepper sauce

1/2 teaspoon salt

1/4 teaspoon freshly ground black pepper

1 teaspoon olive oil

1 cup shelled frozen baby shrimp, thawed

3 scallions, thinly sliced

1/2 teaspoon minced garlic

1. In a medium bowl, beat the egg whites, eggs, water, hot-pepper sauce, salt, and black pepper until blended.

2. In a large nonstick skillet over medium-high heat, heat the oil. Cook the shrimp, scallions, and garlic for 30 seconds.

3. Reduce the heat to medium-low and add the egg mixture. As the mixture begins to set on the bottom of the pan, scrape it up with a spatula until all of the egg is set.

Serves: 4 • Prep Time: 5 MINUTES • Total Time: 10 MINUTES

# Easy Veggie Omelet

*If you're bothered by the odor that lingers on your fingers after chopping onions, rub your hands over a stainless steel spoon or bowl under warm running water. This trick also works well after handling garlic and leeks.*

1 teaspoon olive oil

1/2 cup chopped fresh spinach

1/4 cup chopped onion

1/4 cup sliced mushrooms

1 clove garlic, minced

4 large egg whites, lightly beaten

1/4 cup shredded reduced-fat, low-sodium Cheddar cheese

1. In a small nonstick skillet over medium-high heat, heat the oil. Cook the spinach, onion, mushrooms, and garlic for 3 minutes, stirring occasionally, or until the vegetables start to soften.

2. Add the egg whites and cook for 4 minutes, turning once, or until set. Sprinkle with the cheese and cook for 1 minute longer, or until the cheese is melted.

Serves: 2 • Prep Time: 10 MINUTES • Total Time: 20 MINUTES

Breakfasts

# Quick Tomato Omelet

*This hearty breakfast is faster than a take-out breakfast sandwich and much more delicious. Healthier too!*

1 large egg

4 large egg whites

2 tablespoons chopped chives or scallions

1 tablespoon water

¼ teaspoon salt

¼ teaspoon ground black pepper

1 tablespoon olive oil, divided

2 plum tomatoes, quartered lengthwise and thinly sliced, divided

2 tablespoons crumbled ricotta salata cheese or goat cheese, divided

Tomato slices for garnish (optional)

Chopped chives for garnish (optional)

1. In a medium bowl, whisk together the eggs, egg whites, chives or scallions, water, salt, and pepper until blended.

2. Heat ½ tablespoon of the oil in a large nonstick skillet over medium heat. Add half of the egg mixture (a scant ½ cup) and cook for 2 minutes, occasionally lifting the edges of the egg mixture with a spatula and tilting the pan, allowing the uncooked mixture to flow underneath.

3. When the eggs are almost set, spoon half of the plum tomatoes and cheese down the center of the omelet. Loosen the edges of the omelet with a spatula and fold the two sides over the filling. Slide out onto a plate.

4. Repeat with the remaining oil and egg and tomato mixtures. Serve garnished with the tomato slices and chives, if desired.

**Serves: 2 • Prep Time: 5 MINUTES • Total Time: 10 MINUTES**

# Goat Cheese and Red Onion Omelet

*While red onion gives a fresh, zesty flavor to this omelet, any onion—yellow, green, or sweet—would be just as delicious.*

2 teaspoons olive oil

1 red onion, thinly sliced

½ teaspoon dried thyme

4 large egg whites

1 large egg

½ teaspoon salt

¼ cup crumbled goat cheese

1. In a medium ovenproof nonstick skillet over medium heat, heat the oil. Cook the onion and thyme for 10 minutes, or until softened.

2. In a large bowl, beat the egg whites, egg, and salt. Add the egg mixture to the skillet and cook over medium-low heat for 3 minutes or until the eggs are just set in the center, tilting the skillet and gently lifting the edges of the eggs from the sides of the skillet to let the uncooked portion flow underneath.

3. Sprinkle the cheese over half of the omelet. Fold the omelet over the cheese.

**Serves: 2 • Prep Time: 5 MINUTES • Total Time: 20 MINUTES**

# Frittata with Smoked Salmon and Scallions

*Consider this frittata a perfect choice for a lunch or potluck. While smoked salmon is an expensive ingredient, you only need a small amount to make this dish shine.*

2 teaspoons olive oil

6 scallions, coarsely chopped

6 large egg whites

4 large eggs

$\frac{1}{2}$ teaspoon dried tarragon

$\frac{1}{4}$ cup cold water

2 ounces thinly sliced smoked salmon, cut into $\frac{1}{2}$"-wide pieces

$\frac{1}{2}$ cup chopped fresh basil, arugula, or spinach for garnish (optional)

1. Preheat the oven to 350°F. In a large ovenproof nonstick skillet over medium heat, heat the oil. Cook the scallions, stirring occasionally, for 1 minute, or until soft.

2. In a large bowl, whisk the egg whites, eggs, tarragon, and water until well blended. Pour the mixture into the skillet and lay the salmon pieces on top. Cover the skillet and cook for 2 minutes, or until the edges begin to set.

3. Uncover the skillet, place it in the oven, and bake for 6 minutes or until firm, golden, and puffed. Garnish with fresh basil, arugula, or spinach, if desired.

**Serves: 6 • Prep Time: 10 MINUTES • Total Time: 20 MINUTES**

# Zucchini Frittata

*Whip up this tasty dish on the weekend for at-the-ready breakfasts during the week. Simply refrigerate any leftovers and warm them in the microwave for 1 minute on high, or until desired temperature.*

2 teaspoons olive oil

1 small zucchini, chopped

2 large scallions, thinly sliced

½ teaspoon dried thyme

6 large egg whites

2 large eggs

1 tablespoon water

¼ teaspoon freshly ground black pepper

3 tablespoons grated Parmesan cheese, divided

1. Preheat the broiler. Heat the oil in a 10" ovenproof nonstick skillet over medium heat. Cook the zucchini for 5 minutes, stirring occasionally. Add the scallions and thyme and cook for 3 minutes longer, or until the zucchini is just tender.

2. Meanwhile, in a medium bowl, whisk together the eggs, egg whites, water, pepper, and 2 tablespoons of the cheese.

3. Add the egg mixture to the skillet and cook for 5 minutes, occasionally lifting the edges with a spatula and tilting the pan, allowing the uncooked mixture to flow underneath. (The eggs will be set on the bottom but still moist on the top.)

4. Remove from the heat and top with the remaining 1 tablespoon cheese.

5. Broil 4" from the heat for 2 minutes, or until the eggs are set on the top. Cut into quarters.

**Serves: 4 • Prep Time: 10 MINUTES • Total Time: 25 MINUTES**

Breakfasts

# Spinach-Tomato Frittata

*Frozen or fresh spinach turns this frittata into a nutrient-packed breakfast feast. As it's ready in 15 minutes or less, you can enjoy this dish any time of day.*

10 ounces fresh baby spinach or 1 package (10 ounces) frozen chopped spinach, thawed and squeezed dry

5 large egg whites

3 large eggs

2 scallions, thinly sliced

1 tablespoon olive oil

1 cup grape or cherry tomatoes, halved

1 cup shredded mozzarella cheese

1. Preheat the broiler. In a large bowl, combine the spinach, egg whites, eggs, and scallions. Beat with a fork until well blended.

2. In a large ovenproof nonstick skillet over medium heat, heat the oil. Pour the egg mixture into the skillet and scatter the tomatoes on top. Cover the skillet and cook for 4 minutes, or until the eggs are set around the edges.

3. Broil 5" from the heat for 4 minutes, or until the frittata is lightly browned and the center is set. Top with the cheese. Cover and let stand for 1 minute, or until the cheese melts.

**Serves: 4 • Prep Time: 5 MINUTES • Total Time: 15 MINUTES**

# INGREDIENT GUIDE: *Eggs*

**TO SELECT THE BEST EGGS,** look for:

- AA grade eggs, which are the freshest, with the firmest yolks and smallest air pockets

- Shells free of cracks (shell color is an indication of the breed of chicken and has nothing to do with quality)

**TO STORE,** keep unbroken eggs in their carton on a shelf in the refrigerator (typically, a refrigerator door is not cold enough). Properly stored eggs will be safe to use for about 1 month.

**TO TEST FOR FRESHNESS,** put a whole egg in a shallow glass of water. A fresh egg will sink and lie flat on the bottom of the glass. A week-old egg will sit near the bottom but will bob slightly in the water. A 3-week-old egg will not stand on end, and a rotten egg will float to the surface. This happens because, as an egg ages, the air pocket inside the shell expands until the egg becomes buoyant. Older eggs, with developed air pockets, are easier to peel when making hard-cooked eggs. Whites from older eggs are also easier to whip.

**TO REPLACE WHOLE EGGS WITH EGG WHITES,** substitute 2 egg whites for each whole egg. When you need a very accurate measurement, replace each whole egg with 3 tablespoons egg white. To facilitate measuring, whisk the egg whites with a pinch of salt to help break down the egg protein and loosen the texture.

---

**DID YOU KNOW?** *Legend has it that each pleat on the classic chef's toque (traditionally 100) represents the many ways that eggs can be prepared.*

# Green Eggs and Ham Cups

*This recipe makes enough for a small crowd. Alternately, you can refrigerate the leftovers for several quick breakfasts.*

6 large egg whites

3 large eggs

1 package (10 ounces) frozen chopped spinach, thawed and squeezed dry

1/2 cup shredded reduced-fat Cheddar cheese

1/2 green bell pepper, finely chopped

1 small onion, finely chopped

1/4 cup chopped ham steak

1. Preheat the oven to 350°F. Coat a 12-cup muffin pan with cooking spray.

2. In a large bowl, whisk the egg whites and eggs. Stir in the spinach, cheese, pepper, onion, and ham. Mix well. Evenly divide the mixture among the muffin cups.

3. Bake for 20 minutes, or until an inserted toothpick comes out clean.

**Serves: 6 • Prep Time: 5 MINUTES • Total Time: 25 MINUTES**

# Asparagus-Swiss Quiche

*Here's another make-ahead breakfast. Slices of quiche are perfect to heat up quickly in the microwave oven just before eating.*

| | |
|---|---|
| 1 tablespoon water | 1½ cups 1% milk |
| 1 pound asparagus, trimmed and cut into 1½" pieces | 1 cup shredded reduced-fat Swiss cheese |
| 4 scallions, thinly sliced | 2 teaspoons Dijon mustard |
| 4 large egg whites | ¼ teaspoon salt |
| 2 large eggs | ¼ teaspoon ground black pepper |

1. Preheat the oven to 350°F. Coat a 9" quiche or pie plate with cooking spray.

2. In a nonstick skillet, heat the water over medium-high heat. Cook the asparagus and scallions, stirring, for 5 minutes, or until tender-crisp.

3. Meanwhile, in a large bowl, whisk together the egg whites, eggs, milk, cheese, mustard, salt, and pepper. Stir in the asparagus mixture. Pour into the prepared pan.

4. Bake for 40 minutes, or until a knife inserted in the center comes out clean. Let stand for 10 minutes before serving.

**Serves: 8 • Prep Time: 10 MINUTES • Total Time: 1 HOUR 5 MINUTES**

# Sausage, Egg, and Vegetable Casserole

*This delicious breakfast dish is quite versatile. Change it up by substituting kale, broccoli rabe, or broccoli for the escarole.*

1 pound sweet Italian turkey sausage, casings removed

1½ teaspoons olive oil

½ small head escarole, chopped

2 zucchini, halved and thinly sliced

1 red bell pepper, chopped

1 small red onion, halved and thinly sliced

¼ teaspoon salt

¼ teaspoon freshly ground black pepper

6 large egg whtes

2 large eggs

½ cup 2% milk

¼ cup grated Parmesan cheese

1. Preheat the oven to 350°F. Coat an 8" x 8" baking dish with cooking spray.

2. In a large nonstick skillet over medium-high heat, cook the sausage for 8 minutes, or until half-cooked, stirring occasionally and breaking the meat into bite-size pieces. Spread over the bottom of the prepared baking dish.

3. Heat the oil in the same skillet over medium heat. Cook the escarole, zucchini, bell pepper, onion, salt, and black pepper for 10 minutes, stirring occasionally, or until the vegetables are tender and the liquid evaporates. Let cool for 10 minutes. Spread over the sausage.

4. In a large bowl, whisk together the egg whites, eggs, milk, and cheese. Pour over the vegetables. Bake for 40 to 45 minutes, or until the eggs are set. Cut into squares to serve.

**Serves: 6 • Prep Time: 30 MINUTES • Total Time: 1 HOUR 15 MINUTES**

# Turkey Breakfast Sausage Patties

*These tasty sausage patties will help you control your sodium intake. Compared to prepared links that can have close to 400 milligrams of sodium per serving and almost six times the fat, these homemade sausage patties are a better nutritional value. Make up a batch on the weekend and reheat in the microwave oven during the week.*

¼ cup grated apple

1½ teaspoons freshly ground black pepper

1½ teaspoons ground sage

½ teaspoon salt

½ teaspoon onion powder

1¼ pounds extra lean ground turkey

2 teaspoons olive oil, divided

1. In a large bowl, combine the apple, pepper, sage, salt, and onion powder and mix with a fork until blended. Add the turkey and mix gently until the seasonings are evenly distributed. Roll into small balls (about 1") and flatten into patties.

2. In a large nonstick skillet over medium-high heat, heat 1 teaspoon of the oil. Cook half of the patties in the skillet for 5 minutes, or until the meat is no longer pink. Add the remaining 1 teaspoon oil and repeat with the remaining patties.

**Serves: 8 • Prep Time: 10 MINUTES • Total Time: 20 MINUTES**

Breakfasts

# Creamy Broccoli Soup

*Serve this hearty soup with eggs or even roasted chicken, turkey, or pork. Use most of the stalks of the broccoli along with the florets, as they have plenty of nutrients and fiber.*

2 tablespoons olive oil

1 large onion, chopped

1 teaspoon dried thyme

2 cloves garlic, chopped

1 carton (32 ounces) chicken or vegetable broth

2 pounds broccoli, chopped

$\frac{1}{2}$ teaspoon salt

$\frac{1}{4}$ teaspoon freshly ground black pepper

8 ounces soft silken tofu, rinsed and coarsely chopped

Broccoli florets for garnish (optional)

1. In a large pot or Dutch oven over medium heat, heat the oil. Cook the onion and thyme for 5 minutes, stirring occasionally, until soft and translucent. Add the garlic and cook, stirring, for 1 minute. Add the broth, increase the heat to high, cover, and bring to a boil.

2. Add the broccoli, salt, and pepper and return to a boil. Reduce the heat to low and simmer for 15 minutes, uncovered, or until the vegetables are very tender. Stir in the tofu.

3. Working in batches, transfer the soup to a blender (or use an immersion blender) and puree until smooth. Return the soup to the pot. Divide among 4 bowls and top each serving with the broccoli florets, if desired.

**Serves: 4 • Prep Time: 20 MINUTES • Total Time: 50 MINUTES**

# SOUPS and SIDES

# Butternut Squash Soup

*If you're lucky enough to have leftovers of this bursting-with-flavor soup, it is actually better the next day. If you like a kick in your meals, stir in a dash of hot sauce before serving.*

1 butternut squash, halved and seeded

1 sweet onion, quartered

$\frac{1}{2}$ teaspoon curry powder

$\frac{1}{2}$ teaspoon salt

$\frac{1}{4}$ teaspoon ground black pepper

2 cups reduced-sodium chicken broth

Parsley sprigs for garnish (optional)

1. Preheat the oven to 300°F. Coat a 13" x 9" baking dish with cooking spray. Place the squash cut-side down on the baking dish and arrange the onion around it. Bake for 1 hour, or until the squash is tender. Remove from the oven and set aside until the squash is cool enough to handle, then remove the skin.

2. In a food processor, blend the squash, onion, curry powder, salt, and pepper. Add the broth as needed to thin the mixture to a smooth paste. Transfer the squash mixture to a large saucepot. Over medium heat, stir in the remaining chicken broth. Cook for 5 minutes, stirring occasionally, or until heated through. Divide among 6 bowls and garnish with parsley, if desired.

**Serves: 6 • Prep Time: 10 MINUTES • Total Time: 1 HOUR 10 MINUTES**

# Easy Vegetable Soup

*This delicious soup can be the basis for so many combinations turning it into a main dish. Try adding shredded chicken or turkey for a hearty soup. For a Tex-Mex flavor, eliminate the thyme and stir in cubed pork loin; 1 cup fat-free, sugar-free salsa; and some chopped cilantro. Or any hearty fish like shrimp, scallops, or cubed cod will also make a great meal—try with tarragon instead of the thyme.*

1 tablespoon olive oil

1 onion, chopped

1 rib celery, chopped

1 clove garlic, chopped

1 teaspoon dried thyme

$\frac{1}{4}$ teaspoon salt

$\frac{1}{4}$ teaspoon pepper

$2\frac{1}{2}$ cups vegetable or chicken broth

1 package (5 to 6 ounces) baby spinach

1 large tomato, chopped

1. In a medium saucepan over medium-high heat, warm the oil. Cook the onion, celery, garlic, and thyme, stirring occasionally, for 5 minutes, or until the onion is soft.

2. Add the broth, salt and pepper and bring to a boil. Reduce the heat to low and cook for 5 minutes for the flavors to blend. Stir in the spinach and tomato and cook for 3 minutes or until the spinach wilts.

**Serves: 4 • Prep Time: 5 MINUTES • Total Time: 20 MINUTES**

# Tex-Mex Tomato Soup

*Tomatoes are a top source of lycopene. In a large study, researchers found that women with high levels of the antioxidant had a 34 percent reduced risk of cardiovascular disease compared with women with lower levels. Those who got plenty of lycopene were also more likely to have higher blood levels of other beneficial carotenoids such as lutein and beta-carotene.*

1 tablespoon olive oil

1 rib celery, chopped

1 red bell pepper, chopped

1 onion, chopped

$\frac{1}{4}$ teaspoon salt

1 can (28 ounces) no-salt-added diced tomatoes

2 cups water

1 can (15 ounces) no-salt-added black beans, rinsed and drained

2 tablespoons chipotle pepper sauce

$\frac{1}{2}$ cup chopped fresh cilantro

Juice of 1 lime (optional)

1. In a large pot or Dutch oven over medium-high heat, heat the oil. Cook the celery, pepper, and onion for 10 minutes, or until browned. Add the salt, tomatoes (with juice), and water. Add the beans and chipotle sauce and stir to blend. Bring to a simmer.

2. Reduce the heat to low and simmer for 25 minutes. Stir in the cilantro and lime juice (if using) just before serving.

**Serves: 6 • Prep Time: 10 MINUTES • Total Time: 50 MINUTES**

# Chinese Chicken Soup

*Serve this comforting clear soup as a warming one-dish meal. The tofu boosts the protein profile while keeping the saturated fat low.*

1 large boneless, skinless chicken breast (about 8 ounces), cut into 1" cubes

1 tablespoon reduced-sodium soy sauce

$\frac{1}{2}$ teaspoon freshly ground black pepper

1 teaspoon dark sesame oil

1 onion, chopped

2 small zucchini, cut lengthwise and sliced into half moons

6 cups reduced-sodium chicken broth

8 ounces firm tofu, cut into $\frac{1}{2}$" cubes

$\frac{1}{2}$ cup chopped fresh cilantro

$\frac{1}{3}$ cup chopped scallions

1 teaspoon lime juice

1. In a shallow nonmetal dish, combine the chicken, soy sauce, and pepper. Toss to coat. Let stand for 10 minutes.

2. In a large pot or Dutch oven over medium heat, heat the oil. Cook the onion and zucchini for 5 minutes, stirring occasionally, or until the vegetables are soft. Add the broth and bring to a boil. Reduce the heat to medium. Cover and cook, stirring occasionally, for 20 minutes. Add the chicken and marinade. Cook for 5 to 7 minutes, or until the chicken is no longer pink in the center.

3. Add the tofu, cilantro, and scallions. Cook for 1 minute, or until the tofu is hot. Stir in the lime juice.

**Serves: 6 • Prep Time: 10 MINUTES • Total Time: 45 MINUTES**

# Miso Soup with Asparagus and Broiled Salmon

*Miso, or bean paste, is a culinary mainstay in Japan. It comes in an assortment of colors and flavors, and it is a great source of protein. Spice this soup up with a sprinkle of sliced scallion or red pepper flakes.*

2 tablespoons miso paste, divided

1 tablespoon reduced-sodium soy sauce

4 salmon fillets, skinned (about 4 ounces each)

2 teaspoons dark sesame oil

2 cloves garlic, minced

1½ teaspoons minced fresh ginger

3 cups vegetable broth

1 medium head bok choy, chopped

1 pound asparagus, cut into 1" pieces

2 cups bean sprouts

2 scallions, chopped

1. In a pie plate, stir together 1 tablespoon of the miso paste and the soy sauce. Add the salmon and turn to coat. Set aside.

2. Preheat the broiler. Coat the broiler-pan rack with cooking spray.

3. In a large saucepan over medium heat, cook the oil, garlic, and ginger, stirring, for 2 minutes, or until fragrant. Add the vegetable broth, increase the heat, cover, and bring to a boil. Reduce the heat to medium. Add the bok choy and asparagus. Cover and cook for 5 minutes, or until tender-crisp. Add the bean sprouts and scallions and remove from the heat. Stir in the remaining 1 tablespoon miso and cover to keep warm.

4. After adding the vegetables to the broth, begin to cook the salmon. Broil the salmon 5" from the heat source for 8 to 10 minutes, or until browned and just until opaque. Transfer the salmon to soup bowls, ladle the soup on top, and serve immediately.

**Serves: 4 • Prep Time: 20 MINUTES • Total Time: 25 MINUTES**

# Spanish Seafood Soup

*Seafood stews are fun to prepare because you can vary them to your taste. Any white-fleshed fish fillets—halibut, cod, or tilapia—can replace the flounder. Scallops can stand in for the shrimp. And small mussels can take the place of the clams.*

1 tablespoon olive oil

½ onion, chopped

½ red or yellow bell pepper, chopped

2 cloves garlic, minced

2 cups chicken broth

1 cup water

½ cup canned diced tomatoes with juice

2 tablespoons sherry vinegar or white wine vinegar

¼ teaspoon salt

8 littleneck clams

12 ounces flounder fillets, cut into 1" chunks

4 ounces peeled and deveined medium shrimp

2 tablespoons minced fresh basil or parsley

1. In a large pot or Dutch oven over medium heat, heat the oil. Cook the onion, pepper, and garlic for 5 minutes, stirring occasionally, or until the vegetables are soft. Add the broth, water, tomatoes, vinegar, and salt. Cover and bring almost to a boil. Reduce the heat to low and simmer for 10 minutes for the flavors to blend.

2. Add the clams, flounder, and shrimp. Cover and cook over medium-high heat for 5 minutes, or until the clams open and the fish and shrimp are opaque. Discard any unopened clams. Sprinkle with the basil or parsley.

**Serves: 4 • Prep Time: 10 MINUTES • Total Time: 35 MINUTES**

# Creole Catfish Chowder

*This irresistible dish sings with signature Creole flavors—scallions, celery, bell pepper, parsley, and, of course, peppery Creole seasoning. For the most authentic flavor, stick with catfish. If catfish isn't available, use another mild whitefish such as cod or haddock.*

1 tablespoon olive oil

6 scallions, chopped

2 ribs celery, chopped

2 large cloves garlic, minced

1 red bell pepper, chopped

2 cups fish, vegetable, or chicken broth, preferably reduced-sodium

1 can (14 ounces) diced tomatoes

$\frac{1}{2}$ pound green beans, cut into 2" pieces

1 teaspoon dried marjoram leaves

1 teaspoon dried oregano leaves

$\frac{1}{2}$ teaspoon Creole seasoning

1 pound catfish, cut into 1" pieces

1 tablespoon chopped fresh parsley

1. In a large pot over medium-high heat, heat the oil. Cook the scallions, celery, garlic, and pepper for 10 minutes, stirring occasionally, or until lightly browned. Stir in the broth, tomatoes (with juice), green beans, marjoram, oregano, and Creole seasoning. Bring to a boil. Reduce the heat to low, cover, and simmer for 15 minutes, or until the vegetables are tender.

2. Add the fish. Cover and simmer for 10 minutes, or until the fish is opaque. Stir in the parsley just before serving.

**Serves: 4 • Prep Time: 10 MINUTES • Total Time: 50 MINUTES**

# Spicy Sausage Soup

*Mushrooms lend a hearty, almost meatlike texture to this soup. In fact, a study found that people who substitute mushrooms for meat consume fewer calories and feel just as satisfied as when they eat meat-heavy meals.*

1 tablespoon olive oil

1 pound precooked spicy chicken
  sausage, sliced

1 pound sliced mushrooms

¼ cup water

6 cups low-sodium chicken broth

4 cups chopped kale

¼ teaspoon dried thyme

1. In a large pot or Dutch oven over medium-high heat, heat the oil. Add the sausage and cook for 5 minutes, or until brown. Remove to a paper towel–lined plate.

2. To the same pot, add the mushrooms and cook for 5 to 8 minutes, or until soft and browned. Add the water, scraping up the sausage bits stuck to the bottom of the pan. Add the broth, kale, and thyme. Bring to a boil over high heat. Reduce the heat to low, cover, and simmer for 20 minutes, or until the kale is tender and the flavors blend.

3. Stir in the reserved sausage. Simmer for 5 minutes, or until hot.

**Serves: 4 • Prep Time: 10 MINUTES • Total Time: 45 MINUTES**

Soups and Sides

# Pepper Steak Soup

*This hearty soup is a one-dish meal. Bursting with vegetables and slices of meat, this is sure to become a favorite.*

12 ounces well-trimmed lean boneless beef top round

½ teaspoon salt, divided

½ teaspoon ground black pepper

4 cups beef broth

½ cup tomato sauce

½ teaspoon dried Italian seasoning

1 tablespoon olive oil

2 green bell peppers, cut into strips

1 onion, halved and thinly sliced

4 cloves garlic, minced

3 tablespoons water, divided

1½ cups halved cherry tomatoes

1. Thinly slice the beef on the diagonal into ¼"-thick slices. Cut large pieces in half. Sprinkle with ¼ teaspoon of the salt and the black pepper. Set aside.

2. In a large saucepan, stir together the beef broth, tomato sauce, and Italian seasoning. Cover and bring to a boil over high heat. Reduce the heat to low and cover and simmer for 10 minutes.

3. Meanwhile, in a large nonstick skillet over medium-high heat, heat the oil. Cook half the beef slices, turning once, for 2 minutes, or until browned. Transfer to a bowl. Repeat with the remaining beef.

4. In the same skillet, place the bell peppers, onion, garlic, and the remaining ¼ teaspoon salt. Toss to mix well and add 2 tablespoons of the water. Lower the heat to medium and cook, stirring often, for 10 minutes, or until the vegetables are tender. If the pan gets dry, add the remaining 1 tablespoon water. Add the tomatoes and cook, stirring often, for 5 minutes, or until softened.

5. Add the beef and any juices and the vegetables to the broth mixture. Warm through but don't boil.

**Serves: 4 • Prep Time: 20 MINUTES • Total Time: 45 MINUTES**

# Tomato-Turkey Stew with Gremolata

*This lemony stew is served with gremolata, a lively mixture of garlic, parsley, and lemon peel. If you prefer, chicken or pork can replace the turkey. Before juicing the lemon for the stew, use a zester to remove the peel for the gremolata.*

**STEW**

1 tablespoon olive oil

6 scallions, chopped

2 cloves garlic, minced

1 large red bell pepper, finely chopped

1 rib celery, thinly sliced

1 pound boneless, skinless turkey breast, cut into 1" cubes

1 can (14.5 ounces) diced tomatoes

1 cup reduced-sodium chicken broth

Juice of 1 lemon

1 teaspoon dried Italian herb seasoning

½ teaspoon salt

**GREMOLATA**

1 tablespoon finely chopped fresh parsley

1 teaspoon grated lemon peel

1 clove garlic, minced

1 teaspoon salt

1. *To make the stew:* In a large saucepan or Dutch oven over medium-high heat, heat the oil. Cook the scallions, garlic, pepper, and celery, stirring frequently, for 2 minutes. Add the turkey and cook, stirring, for 10 minutes, or until lightly browned. Add the tomatoes (with juice), broth, lemon juice, Italian herb seasoning, and salt. Bring to a boil. Reduce the heat to low, cover, and simmer for 10 minutes. Uncover and simmer for 10 minutes, or until the stew thickens.

2. *To make the gremolata:* Meanwhile, in a small bowl, combine the parsley, lemon peel, garlic, and salt. Sprinkle over each serving of the stew.

**Serves: 4 • Prep Time: 10 MINUTES • Total Time: 45 MINUTES**

# INGREDIENT GUIDE: *Tomatoes*

TO SELECT THE BEST TOMATOES, look for:

- Farmers' markets and local produce stands in the warm summer months and early fall when they are at the peak of their growing season

- Firm (but not hard) tomatoes that are heavy for their size and have a sweet tomato aroma

- Yellow tomatoes, which are sweeter and less acidic, for salads; plum or Roma tomatoes if you're planning on making a sauce

TO STORE, keep fresh tomatoes in a cool but not cold spot. Never refrigerate a tomato. Temperatures below 55°F make tomatoes spongy and destroy their flavor.

DID YOU KNOW? There are more than 4,000 varieties of tomatoes. Some are as small as marbles. The Ponderosa is the giant, weighing more than 3 pounds.

TO RIPEN END-OF-SEASON GREEN TOMATOES, layer them, stem side down, between sheets of newspaper in a box. Store the box in a cool location.

TO PEEL TOMATOES, cut a small X at the base of several tomatoes and drop them into a pot of boiling water just until the skins begin to loosen, 10 to 15 seconds. Remove them with a sieve or a pair of tongs and hold each tomato under cold running water. The peel will slip off easily.

TO PRESERVE LEFTOVER FRESH TOMATOES, freeze the tomatoes whole. Run under warm water to remove the peels, then use the whole frozen tomatoes to make sauce. You can also make fresh tomato sauce and freeze it. Or make a big batch of salsa and freeze it in zip-top freezer bags. Homemade salsa (even frozen and thawed) beats the jarred varieties any day.

FASCINATING FACT: *Ketchup was sold in the 1830s as medicine.*

# Asparagus with Tomato Vinaigrette

*Look for jars of sun-dried tomatoes packed in olive oil, often found in the supermarket produce section.*

2¾ pounds asparagus, tough ends trimmed

1 tablespoon olive oil

¼ teaspoon salt

1 tablespoon balsamic vinegar

2 tablespoons chopped sun-dried tomatoes packed in olive oil, plus 2 tablespoons of the oil

1. Preheat the broiler. Arrange the asparagus on a baking sheet and drizzle with the oil and salt. Broil 6" to 8" from the heat source for 5 minutes, turning occasionally, or until lightly browned. Transfer to a serving platter.

2. Meanwhile, in a small bowl, whisk together the vinegar and the oil from the sun-dried tomato jar until blended. Whisk in the sun-dried tomatoes. Drizzle over the asparagus.

**Serves: 4 • Prep Time: 5 MINUTES • Total Time: 10 MINUTES**

Soups and Sides

# Curried Roasted Cauliflower with Flaxseeds

*A trick for getting great browning and caramelization when roasting cruciferous vegetables like cauliflower, broccoli, and Brussels sprouts is to start with veggies that are completely dry. Wash and air-dry in advance or toss them around in a kitchen towel to soak up as much water as possible if you're pressed for time.*

1 tablespoon olive oil

2 tablespoons curry powder

½ teaspoon salt

¼ teaspoon freshly ground black pepper

1 large head cauliflower, cut into bite-size pieces

3 tablespoons ground flaxseeds

Juice of 1½ limes (about 3 tablespoons)

2 tablespoons fresh cilantro leaves

1. Preheat the oven to 400°F. Coat a baking sheet with cooking spray. In a small bowl, stir together the oil, curry powder, salt, and pepper.

2. Make a pile of the cauliflower on the baking sheet. Pour the oil mixture over the cauliflower and toss to coat. Spread the cauliflower evenly on the baking sheet and roast for 15 minutes, turning occasionally, until lightly browned. Sprinkle with the flaxseeds and toss. Roast for 10 minutes, or until the cauliflower is tender.

3. Transfer to a serving bowl. Add the lime juice and cilantro and toss to blend.

**Serves: 4 • Prep Time: 5 MINUTES • Total Time: 30 MINUTES**

# Brussels Sprouts with Orange Sauce

*Roasting Brussels sprouts creates an addictive caramelized flavor that pairs perfectly with this orange-infused sauce.*

2 pounds Brussels sprouts, washed and thoroughly dried

1 tablespoon olive oil

½ teaspoon salt

¼ teaspoon ground black pepper

½ cup low-fat plain Greek yogurt

3 tablespoons orange juice

1 teaspoon orange zest

1. Preheat the oven to 400°F. Trim the Brussels sprout stems, leaving the sprouts intact, and discard any damaged outer leaves.

2. Place on a baking sheet and toss with the oil, salt, and pepper. Roast for 30 minutes or until deep golden brown, turning once or twice.

3. Meanwhile, in a small bowl, whisk together the yogurt and orange juice. Serve with the Brussels sprouts.

**Serves: 6 • Prep Time: 5 MINUTES • Total Time: 35 MINUTES**

# Sautéed Cabbage and Onion *(left)*

*Serve this zesty side dish with roasted fish, poultry, or pork for a quick dinner.*

1 tablespoon olive oil

1 pound red cabbage, shredded

1 large red onion, sliced

3 to 4 tablespoons balsamic vinegar

In a large skillet over medium heat, heat the oil. Cook the cabbage and onion for 10 minutes, or until tender. Stir in the vinegar and cook for 1 minute.

Serves: 6 • Prep Time: 5 MINUTES • Total Time: 15 MINUTES

# Sautéed Cherry Tomatoes with White Beans

*White beans go perfectly with the other Italian flavors in this dish.*

1 teaspoon olive oil

3 large scallions, chopped

2 teaspoons thinly sliced fresh sage

3 cups cherry tomatoes, halved

1 cup canned no-salt-added white beans, rinsed and drained

$\frac{1}{4}$ teaspoon salt

$\frac{1}{8}$ teaspoon freshly ground black pepper

In a large nonstick skillet over medium heat, heat the oil. Cook the scallions for 1 minute, stirring, or until softened. Add the sage, tomatoes, and white beans. Cook for 2 minutes, stirring frequently, or until the tomatoes become soft. Stir in the salt and pepper just before serving.

Serves: 4 • Prep Time: 10 MINUTES • Total Time: 15 MINUTES

# Grilled Eggplant

*The meaty texture of eggplant makes it a fitting substitute in many dishes. Use it to replace the noodles in traditional lasagna or cut the grilled eggplant into bite-size pieces for a smoky addition to a main-dish salad.*

4 large eggplants, unpeeled, cut lengthwise into 1"-thick slices, divided

2 teaspoons kosher salt, divided

4 tablespoons olive oil

$\frac{1}{2}$ teaspoon freshly ground black pepper

1. Layer several paper towels on a baking sheet. Place half of the eggplant on top in a single layer. Sprinkle with 1 teaspoon of the salt and cover with paper towels. Arrange a second layer of eggplant, sprinkle with the remaining salt, and cover with paper towels. Let the eggplant stand for 30 minutes, then rinse each piece and blot dry. (This helps extract excess water, reducing bitterness and preventing the eggplant from absorbing excess oil during cooking.)

2. Brush both sides of the eggplant slices with oil to coat and transfer to a large bowl. Season the eggplant with the pepper. Heat the grill to medium. Grill the eggplant, with the cover closed, for 15 to 20 minutes, or until browned and tender, turning once. Refrigerate leftovers in an airtight container for a day or two.

**Serves: 8 • Prep Time: 40 MINUTES • Total Time: 1 HOUR**

# SALADS

# Warm Zucchini Salad

*Zucchini as a salad is a great twist on this revered veggie. This delicious dish is perfect served alongside fish, beef, or poultry.*

3 small zucchini

1 tablespoon olive oil

1 small red onion, thinly sliced

3 plum tomatoes, chopped

$\frac{1}{4}$ cup thinly sliced fresh basil

1 tablespoon lemon juice

1. Using a vegetable peeler or mandoline, thinly slice the zucchini lengthwise, about $\frac{1}{16}$" thick.

2. In a large nonstick skillet over medium-high heat, warm the oil. Cook the onion, stirring, for 3 minutes, or until soft. Add the tomatoes and zucchini and cook, stirring, for 5 minutes, or until tender. Toss with the basil and lemon juice.

**Serves: 4 • Prep Time: 5 MINUTES • Total Time: 15 MINUTES**

# Crunchy Fennel Salad

*To slice fennel, chop off the stems and fronds just where the pale bulb turns darker green. Then cut the bulb as you would an onion, first slicing it in half lengthwise (through the bottom and stem ends). Trim and discard the bottom end. Place cut side down and slice crosswise into crescent-shaped pieces.*

2 tablespoons olive oil

Juice of 1 lemon

1 tablespoon rice wine vinegar

$\frac{1}{2}$ teaspoon salt

$\frac{1}{4}$ teaspoon ground black pepper

1 small fennel bulb, sliced

2 ribs celery, sliced

1 cup chopped fresh parsley

$\frac{1}{2}$ small red onion, sliced

In a large bowl, whisk together the oil, lemon juice, vinegar, salt, and pepper. Add the fennel, celery, parsley, and onion. Toss to coat well. Let stand for 30 minutes before serving.

**Serves: 2 • Prep Time: 10 MINUTES • Total Time: 40 MINUTES**

# Tomato-Basil Salad

*This salad is lovely served over grilled fish or chicken. For a hearty meal, line plates with arugula, top with the fish or chicken, and top with the salad.*

4 cups halved cherry tomatoes

$\frac{1}{4}$ cup fresh basil leaves, cut into thin strips

4 teaspoons olive oil

2 teaspoons balsamic vinegar

$\frac{1}{2}$ teaspoon salt

$\frac{1}{4}$ teaspoon cracked black pepper

2 cups arugula (optional)

In a large bowl, combine the tomatoes, basil, olive oil, vinegar, salt, and pepper. Toss to coat well. If desired, serve over the arugula.

**Serves: 4 • Prep Time: 5 MINUTES • Total Time: 5 MINUTES**

# Red Cabbage Slaw

*This salad comes together quickly and is perfect for lunches with some grilled or roasted meats.*

3 tablespoons white wine vinegar

3 tablespoons olive oil

1 tablespoon Dijon mustard

Pinch of stevia

½ head red cabbage, cored and thinly sliced

2 yellow bell peppers, thinly sliced

2 orange bell peppers, thinly sliced

½ cup coarsely chopped fresh flat-leaf parsley

In a large bowl, whisk together the vinegar, oil, mustard, and stevia. Add the cabbage, bell peppers, carrots, and parsley and toss until well blended.

**Serves: 6 • Prep Time: 20 MINUTES • Total Time: 20 MINUTES**

# Smoked Tofu and Greens

*Smoked tofu has been seasoned, baked, and smoked, creating a dense texture and flavorful bite. Look for it in the refrigerated section of your supermarket. Available in natural smoked flavor, smoked tofu is also available in a variety of flavors including Asian, Italian, and Caribbean. Each will work well in this salad.*

2 tablespoons olive oil

1 tablespoon balsamic vinegar

1 teaspoon Dijon mustard

4 marinated sun-dried tomatoes, drained and chopped

¼ teaspoon salt

¼ teaspoon ground black pepper

1 package (8 ounces) smoked tofu, cut into ¾" cubes

1 package (5 or 6 ounces) salad greens, such as baby arugula, baby spinach, or spring mix

In a large bowl, whisk together the oil, vinegar, mustard, tomatoes, salt, and pepper. Add the tofu and greens and toss to blend.

**Serves: 4 • Prep Time: 10 MINUTES • Total Time: 10 MINUTES**

# Broccoli, Chickpea, and Cherry Tomato Salad

*This recipe is especially welcome for those times of the year when fresh lettuce isn't at its best. If time permits, refrigerate the salad for at least 30 minutes before serving to allow the flavors to completely blend.*

3 cups small broccoli florets

2 tablespoons water

1 tablespoon olive oil

1 tablespoon white wine vinegar or white balsamic vinegar

2 teaspoons Dijon mustard

$1/4$ teaspoon salt

$1/4$ teaspoon ground black pepper

$1^1/2$ cups halved cherry tomatoes or grape tomatoes

1 can (15 ounces) chickpeas, rinsed and drained

$1/2$ cup coarsely chopped jarred, drained roasted red peppers

$1/4$ cup sliced scallions

1. Place the broccoli in a microwaveable bowl with the water. Cover loosely with waxed paper and microwave on high for 2 to 3 minutes, or until tender-crisp. Transfer the broccoli to a colander and cool briefly under cold running water. Drain and pat dry with a paper towel.

2. In a large bowl, whisk together the oil, vinegar, mustard, salt, and black pepper. Add the broccoli, tomatoes, chickpeas, roasted red peppers, and scallions and stir to coat well.

**Serves: 4 • Prep Time: 15 MINUTES • Total Time: 15 MINUTES**

Salads

# Spinach Salad with Warm Bacon Vinaigrette

*The Romano cheese on this salad tastes best when cut into shavings (thin slices) rather than grated over the top. To cut a shaving of Romano cheese, drag a vegetable peeler or cheese slicer along the broad side of the block of cheese to create thin slices about 1" wide and 2" long. To make a main-dish salad, garnish each serving with two or three wedges of tomato, a few slices of hard-cooked egg, and a slice of red onion. Or add cold, cooked chicken.*

3 strips bacon

3 tablespoons walnut oil or olive oil

2 tablespoons red wine vinegar or other vinegar

1 teaspoon Dijon mustard (optional)

1 small clove garlic, minced

$\frac{1}{8}$ teaspoon salt

$\frac{1}{8}$ teaspoon freshly ground black pepper

1 bunch (10 ounces) spinach, coarse stems trimmed (about 5 cups loosely packed)

1 small apple, peeled and cut into $\frac{1}{2}$" pieces

8 shavings ($\frac{3}{4}$ ounce) Romano cheese, each about 1" x 2"

1. In a large skillet over medium-low heat, cook the bacon for 8 minutes, turning occasionally, until crisp and browned. Drain on a paper towel–lined plate and keep warm. Drain the fat from the pan.

2. In a medium bowl, whisk the oil, vinegar, mustard (if using), garlic, salt, and pepper. Add to the still-hot pan, stirring to scrape up any browned bits. Keep warm.

3. In a large bowl, combine the spinach and apple. Top with the warm bacon mixture. Toss to coat well. Divide among 4 plates, crumble the bacon over the spinach, and top with the cheese.

**Serves: 4 • Prep Time: 5 MINUTES • Total Time: 15 MINUTES**

# Sardine Salad

*Give wild sardines a chance if you've never tried them. They are very similar to tuna but with a less distinct flavor. In this refreshing salad, just a bit of lemon and tomato is all you need to balance the flavors.*

2 tablespoons olive oil

1 tablespoon fresh lemon juice

1 tablespoon chopped fresh parsley

1 can (4.375 ounces) wild sardines in
water, drained

1 tomato, chopped

2 cups spinach leaves

2 tablespoons pine nuts, toasted

1. In a medium bowl, whisk together the oil, lemon juice, and parsley. Gently stir in the sardines and tomato.

2. Divide the spinach between 2 plates and top with the sardine mixture and pine nuts.

**Serves: 2 • Prep Time: 5 MINUTES • Total Time: 5 MINUTES**

## *Preserving Fresh Herbs*

Herbs are the simplest way to boost the character of a dish. Preserving leftover fresh herbs makes them much easier to use year-round. When herbs are in season or you simply have some left over, pluck the leaves from the stem and plunge them into boiling water for 5 seconds, just until wilted. Drain, pat dry, and chop. For every ¼ cup of chopped herbs, drizzle with 2 teaspoons olive oil and toss well. Line a plate with plastic wrap and dot with teaspoon-size mounds of the oiled herbs. Freeze until the mounds are solid. Peel from the plastic and place in a zip-top freezer bag for up to 6 months. Alternatively, to dry tender herbs, such as basil and parsley, spread them on a mesh screen and leave in a dry, well-ventilated area for 3 to 6 days, or until crumbly. Store the herbs in airtight containers until ready to use.

# Tuna Salad in Lettuce Wrappers

*When you want to explore other fillings for these sandwichlike salads, try substituting canned or cooked salmon or boneless, skinless sardines for the tuna. You can also add 1 chopped hard-cooked egg and ½ teaspoon dried dill to the salad if you need an extra protein boost.*

2 cans (6 ounces each) water-packed tuna, drained

¼ cup mayonnaise

1 teaspoon Dijon mustard

1 tablespoon lemon juice

2 tablespoons finely chopped celery

2 teaspoons capers, drained (optional)

¼ teaspoon salt

⅛ teaspoon freshly ground black pepper

8 large lettuce leaves, such as Boston or leaf

In a large bowl, flake the tuna with a fork. Stir in the mayonnaise, mustard, and lemon juice. Stir in the celery, capers (if using), salt, and pepper. Arrange the lettuce leaves on a work surface with the rib ends closest to you and the "cups" facing up. Evenly divide the tuna salad among the leaves near the rib ends and roll to enclose.

**Serves: 4 • Prep Time: 20 MINUTES • Total Time: 20 MINUTES**

# Tuna and Chickpea Salad in Tomato Cups

*Chickpeas are filling, and they add texture and fiber to this protein-packed tuna salad. Smoked paprika lends savory flavor, but if you don't have any, mild chili powder or regular paprika are good substitutes.*

1 can (15 ounces) chickpeas, rinsed and drained

2 pouches (6.4 ounces each) chunk light tuna in water, drained

⅓ cup chopped jarred Peppadew peppers or roasted red peppers

¼ cup chopped fresh parsley, dill, cilantro, or chives, or a combination

½ teaspoon smoked paprika

⅔ cup 2% plain Greek yogurt

Salt and ground black pepper

4 large beefsteak tomatoes

1. In a large bowl, mash the chickpeas coarsely with a fork, leaving some whole. Add the tuna, peppers, herbs, and paprika and stir to blend well. Add the yogurt and stir well to combine. Season the tuna mixture to taste with the salt and black pepper.

2. Cut each tomato in half crosswise and hollow out the centers with a paring knife and spoon. Place on a plate and evenly divide the tuna mixture among the tomatoes.

**Serves: 4 • Prep Time: 25 MINUTES • Total Time: 25 MINUTES**

Salads

# Salmon Salad in Lettuce Cups

*Wild salmon boasts higher levels of omega-3 fatty acids than farmed salmon. But whatever type of salmon you choose, you'll find these wraps are likely to become a delicious mainstay of your weekly menus.*

3 tablespoons 2% plain Greek yogurt

1 tablespoon reduced-sodium soy sauce

1 tablespoon rice wine vinegar

¼ teaspoon ground ginger

¼ teaspoon garlic powder

¼ teaspoon onion powder

2 cans (5 ounces each) wild salmon, drained

½ rib celery, finely chopped

6 large Bibb or butterhead lettuce leaves

½ medium cucumber, thinly sliced into coins

Seaweed snacks or ribbons of nori, for garnish (optional)

Sliced scallions, for garnish (optional)

1. In a large bowl, whisk together the yogurt, soy sauce, vinegar, ginger, garlic powder, and onion powder. Add the salmon and celery, folding gently until evenly coated.

2. Place the lettuce leaves on a serving plate. Evenly divide the salmon mixture among the leaves. Top with the cucumber coins and seaweed and scallions, if using.

**Serves: 2 • Prep Time: 15 MINUTES • Total Time: 15 MINUTES**

# Toasted Almond Chicken Salad

*Toasting the almonds helps deepen their nutty flavor. Simply place them in a dry skillet over medium-high heat, shake the pan frequently, and toast until they are lightly browned and fragrant.*

3 small chicken breast halves

3 ribs celery, sliced

2 tablespoons minced chives

$1/2$ to $3/4$ cup 2% plain Greek yogurt

$1^1/2$ teaspoons dried tarragon

$1/2$ teaspoon salt

$1/4$ teaspoon ground black pepper

1 bag (8 to 10 ounces) mixed greens

2 tablespoons slivered almonds, toasted

1. Coat a nonstick skillet with cooking spray. Over medium-high heat, cook the chicken breasts in the skillet for 8 minutes, turning once, or until a thermometer inserted into the thickest portion registers 165°F and the juices run clear. Remove the chicken from the heat and let rest for at least 10 minutes. When cool enough to handle, chop the chicken breasts into small pieces.

2. In a large bowl, combine the chicken, celery, chives, yogurt, tarragon, salt, and pepper. Mix lightly. Cover and chill for at least 1 hour, or up to 24 hours. Divide the greens among 4 plates and top with the chicken mixture and almonds.

**Serves: 4 • Prep Time: 20 MINUTES • Total Time: 1 HOUR 30 MINUTES**

# INGREDIENT GUIDE: *Nuts*

**TO SELECT THE BEST NUTS,** look for:

- Whole clean shells with no holes or cracks. Shake the nut if you can, and if it rattles freely, it's likely old and dry.

- Plump, unbroken nutmeats. Any sign of shriveling or discoloration indicates they're past their prime.

**TO STORE,** keep all nuts, whether shelled or unshelled, in a cool, dry place. Shelled nuts should be tightly wrapped and refrigerated for up to 4 weeks or frozen for up to a few months unless they are in a vacuum-packed can. Nuts in the shell can be refrigerated for several months. In general, unsalted nuts stay fresh longer than salted nuts.

**TO TOAST NUTS,** place a single layer of nutmeats in a dry skillet and cook, shaking the pan often, over medium-low heat until the nuts are fragrant and slightly browned, 2 to 3 minutes. Remove from the heat and stir until the nuts cool slightly and emit a pronounced toasted aroma. Because toasted nuts turn rancid more quickly than raw ones, be sure to use them within a few days of toasting.

**TO USE SALTED NUTS** when unsalted nuts are called for, drop the salted nuts into a pot of boiling water for 2 minutes. Drain and dry on a baking sheet in a 250°F oven for 5 minutes.

**DID YOU KNOW?** Pecans have a higher fat content than any other nut (70 percent), giving them a distinguished and complex flavor. Their high fat content also makes them more perishable than most nuts.

---

**FASCINATING FACT:** *Cashews are never sold in the shell because the oil that surrounds the shell is a skin irritant and can cause blisters. Cashews are actually in the same family as poison ivy.*

# Greek Chicken and Chickpea Salad with Tomato Vinaigrette

*The flavors of the Mediterranean shine in this easy main-dish salad. Use lemon pepper seasoning instead of Greek seasoning, if you like.*

**VINAIGRETTE**

¼ cup lemon juice

2 tablespoons white balsamic vinegar

1 clove garlic, crushed

¾ teaspoon Greek seasoning

¼ cup tomato juice

¼ teaspoon salt (optional)

¼ cup olive oil

**SALAD**

1 can (15 ounces) chickpeas, rinsed and drained

2 cups chopped cooked chicken breast

½ cup chopped fresh flat-leaf parsley

½ small cucumber, chopped

5 radishes, sliced

⅓ cup grape or cherry tomatoes, halved

2 tablespoons pitted Kalamata olives

¼ cup crumbled feta cheese

1 small head romaine lettuce, chopped into bite-size pieces

1. *To make the vinaigrette:* In a medium bowl, whisk together the lemon juice, vinegar, garlic, Greek seasoning, tomato juice, and salt (if using) until well blended. Whisk in the oil until emulsified. Set aside.

2. *To make the salad:* In a large bowl, mash the chickpeas with a fork. Add the chicken, parsley, cucumber, radishes, tomatoes, olives, and feta. Drizzle with half of the vinaigrette and toss to coat well. Divide the lettuce and the chickpea mixture among 6 plates. Pass the remaining dressing to use as desired. Or, save it for another recipe.

**Serves: 6 • Prep Time: 20 MINUTES • Total Time: 20 MINUTES**

# Chicken and Asparagus Salad with Tarragon Dressing

*Unexpected guests dropping by for lunch? Serve this elegant salad on a bed of greens, such as a mixture of watercress and Bibb lettuce, a toss of baby greens, or with sliced tomatoes. For an added crunch, top with some toasted nuts.*

1 pound asparagus, tough ends trimmed, cut into 1" pieces

Pinch of salt

¼ cup mayonnaise

1 tablespoon lemon juice

1 teaspoon grated lemon zest

½ teaspoon dried tarragon

½ teaspoon Dijon mustard

½ teaspoon salt

1 rib celery, diagonally sliced

½ small red onion, halved and thinly sliced

2 boneless, skinless chicken breast halves from a rotisserie chicken, shredded

1. In a medium skillet, bring ½" of water to a boil over high heat. Add the asparagus and salt and cook, stirring often, for 4 to 5 minutes, until tender-crisp. Drain and cool briefly under cold running water.

2. In a large bowl, whisk together the mayonnaise, lemon juice and zest, tarragon, mustard, and salt. Add the celery, onion, chicken, and asparagus and toss to coat.

**Serves: 4 • Prep Time: 15 MINUTES • Total Time: 15 MINUTES**

# Grilled Pork Salad

*Here's a great salad recipe to remember when you have a small amount of leftover grilled pork. Of course, grilled chicken would make a fine substitute too.*

2 tablespoons balsamic vinegar

1 tablespoon olive oil

2 cups mixed baby greens

3 ounces grilled pork tenderloin, chopped into bite-size pieces

1 rib celery, sliced

½ red bell pepper, chopped

In a large bowl, whisk together the vinegar and oil. Add the greens and toss until well coated. Top with the pork, celery, and red pepper.

**Serves: 1 • Prep Time: 10 MINUTES • Total Time: 10 MINUTES**

# Asian Stir-Fry Steak Salad

*There's no reason to miss the rice when you have so many delicious flavors packed into a salad that's ready in under an hour. For even better results, plan ahead and let the beef marinate overnight.*

2 tablespoons reduced-sodium soy sauce

1 clove garlic, minced

6 ounces beef tenderloin, thinly sliced

2 teaspoons toasted sesame oil

¼ cup reduced-sodium beef broth

1 medium red bell pepper, sliced

½ onion, sliced into rings

½ pound mushrooms of your choice, sliced

½ head leaf lettuce, torn into bite-size pieces

1. In a shallow glass dish, mix the soy sauce and garlic. Lay the beef slices in the sauce and turn several times to coat. Cover and refrigerate for 30 minutes.

2. In a large nonstick skillet or wok over medium-high heat, heat the oil. Cook the beef and its marinade, stirring constantly, for 5 minutes, or until no longer pink. Transfer the beef to a large bowl and set aside. Add the broth, pepper, onion, and mushrooms to the skillet and cook for 3 minutes, or until the vegetables are bright and tender-crisp. Add to the beef mixture and toss to coat well. Serve over lettuce.

**Serves: 2 • Prep Time: 10 MINUTES • Total Time: 50 MINUTES**

# SEAFOOD

# Spicy Fish with Peppers *(left)*

*This island-style recipe calls for a colorful medley of sweet and hot peppers. Serve with roasted cauliflower or a side salad for a light yet satisfying meal.*

1 green bell pepper, chopped

1 red bell pepper, chopped

¼ cup chopped fresh parsley

1 small jalapeño pepper, seeded and chopped (wear plastic gloves when handling)

Juice of 1 lime

2 tablespoons cider vinegar

4 cloves garlic, minced

4 cod, halibut, or flounder fillets (4 ounces each)

1. In a small bowl, combine the bell peppers, parsley, jalapeño, lime juice, vinegar, and garlic. Let stand at room temperature for 15 minutes.

2. Preheat the oven to 400°F. Coat a 13" x 9" glass baking dish with cooking spray. Place the fish in the baking dish. Top with the pepper mixture. Bake for 10 minutes, or until the fish flakes easily with a fork.

**Serves: 4 • Prep Time: 20 MINUTES • Total Time: 30 MINUTES**

# Grilled Halibut with Tomatoes

*This Mediterranean-inspired entrée is easy enough for a weeknight meal yet worthy of a dinner party. If you can't find slow-roasted tomatoes in your grocery, sun-dried tomatoes will work just as well in this recipe.*

½ cup chopped slow-roasted tomatoes

3 Kalamata olives, pitted and finely chopped

1 tablespoon finely chopped red onion

1 teaspoon red wine vinegar

1 pound halibut fillets

1½ teaspoons olive oil

¼ teaspoon salt

¼ teaspoon ground black pepper

1. In a small bowl, combine the tomatoes, olives, onion, and vinegar. Set aside.

2. Preheat the grill to medium. Brush the halibut with oil to lightly coat, and season with salt and pepper. Grill 6 to 10 minutes, turning once, or until the center of the fish is opaque. Spoon the tomato mixture over the top of the fish just before serving.

**Serves: 4 • Prep Time: 5 MINUTES • Total Time: 15 MINUTES**

Seafood

# Halibut en Papillote

*Cooking en papillote means to cook something in a packet, usually of parchment paper. You may substitute sheets of aluminum foil, which work just as well and are easier to seal when the packets are formed.*

1 medium red onion, very thinly sliced

4 teaspoons olive oil

4 skinless halibut fillets (6 ounces each)

¾ pound asparagus, trimmed

1 plum tomato, seeded and diced

2 tablespoons fresh lemon juice

¼ teaspoon salt

⅛ teaspoon freshly ground black pepper

¼ cup thinly sliced fresh basil leaves

1. Preheat the oven to 450°F. Cut four 18" x 12" sheets of parchment paper or foil. Arrange the parchment with the long side facing you. Fold the sheet in half from short end to short end, and then open it like a book. Place one-fourth of the onion in the center of the right half of the sheet. Drizzle with ¼ teaspoon of the oil. Top the onion with a halibut fillet. Place one-fourth of the asparagus next to the halibut and sprinkle diced tomato over both. Drizzle with ¾ teaspoon oil and ½ tablespoon lemon juice.

2. Repeat with the remaining parchment, onion, oil, halibut, asparagus, tomato, and lemon juice. Sprinkle all the packets with the salt and pepper. Fold the parchment over the halibut mixture, like closing a book, and then tightly crimp the edges to seal the packets.

3. Place the packets on a large baking sheet and bake for 12 minutes, or until the packets have expanded and are puffy. Remove from the oven and set one packet onto each of 4 serving plates. Make a cross in the top of each packet with the tip of a knife and carefully fold back the packet, being mindful of the steam, and sprinkle with the basil.

**Serves: 4 • Prep Time: 20 MINUTES • Total Time: 35 MINUTES**

# Grilled Whitefish with Quick Pesto

*Make this pesto up to 6 hours in advance and cover it with plastic wrap pressed onto the surface to prevent discoloration. This versatile pesto is great served with steak, chicken, or pork. If you find yourself with leftovers, stir a few tablespoons into plain Greek yogurt for a tasty dip for fresh veggies.*

1 cup fresh basil leaves

$\frac{1}{4}$ cup grated Parmesan cheese

$\frac{1}{4}$ cup toasted walnuts

$1\frac{1}{2}$ tablespoons olive oil

$\frac{1}{2}$ teaspoon salt, divided

$\frac{1}{4}$ teaspoon freshly ground black pepper, divided

$\frac{1}{3}$ cup water

$1\frac{1}{4}$ pounds cod, scrod, or other firm whitefish fillet, cut into 4 pieces

1 large red onion, cut into wedges

1 pound asparagus, trimmed

1. In a food processor or blender, combine the basil, cheese, walnuts, oil, $\frac{1}{4}$ teaspoon of the salt, $\frac{1}{8}$ teaspoon of the pepper, and the water. Pulse until smooth. Transfer to a small bowl and cover the surface with plastic wrap. Chill until ready to use.

2. Preheat the grill or heat a grill pan coated with cooking spray over medium-high heat. Season the fish with the remaining $\frac{1}{4}$ teaspoon salt and $\frac{1}{8}$ teaspoon pepper and set aside. Grill the onion for 10 minutes, turning once. Grill the asparagus for 6 minutes, turning occasionally, until softened. Remove to a serving plate. Reduce the heat to medium. Grill the fish, turning once, for 4 minutes, or until the fish flakes easily with a fork. Divide the fish, onion, and asparagus among 4 plates. Drizzle each with the pesto.

**Serves: 4 • Prep Time: 15 MINUTES • Total Time: 35 MINUTES**

# Grilled Salmon with Spicy Cucumbers

*A delicious way to grill salmon is to cook it on a cedar plank. Planks are available in supermarkets and kitchen shops, especially in summer. Be sure to soak the cedar plank in water for at least 2 hours. Lay the cedar plank on a hot grill, and when the plank begins to smoke, lay the fish on it, skin side down, and cook until opaque.*

2 tablespoons chopped fresh mint or cilantro

1 large English cucumber, sliced

2 tablespoons rice wine vinegar

1 teaspoon red pepper flakes

1 salmon fillet (about $\frac{3}{4}$ pound)

$\frac{1}{4}$ teaspoon salt

$\frac{1}{4}$ teaspoon ground black pepper

1. In a medium bowl, combine the mint or cilantro, cucumber, vinegar, and red pepper flakes. Set aside. Sprinkle the salmon with the salt and pepper.

2. Coat the grill grates or a grill pan with cooking spray and preheat the grill. Grill the salmon for 10 minutes with the top closed, or until the salmon is no longer opaque. Top the salmon with the cucumber mixture.

**Serves: 2 • Prep Time: 5 MINUTES • Total Time: 15 MINUTES**

# Oven-Roasted Salmon

*Look for miso in the refrigerated section of supermarkets. In general, the color of miso is an indicator of its flavor. White miso, which is sometimes more light beige in color, has a sweeter, more delicate flavor compared with its darker miso counterparts.*

3 tablespoons white miso

1 tablespoon rice wine vinegar

½ teaspoon reduced-sodium soy sauce

1 teaspoon canola oil

4 wild-caught salmon fillets (6 ounces each)

1 teaspoon toasted sesame seeds

1. Preheat the oven to 400°F. In a small bowl, whisk the miso, vinegar, and soy sauce until blended. Set aside.

2. In a large ovenproof nonstick skillet over medium-high heat, heat the oil. Cook the salmon, skin side up, for 2 to 3 minutes, or until lightly browned. Flip the fish and place the skillet in the oven. Roast about 6 minutes, or until the salmon is opaque. Brush the salmon with the miso mixture and sprinkle with the sesame seeds.

**Serves: 4 • Prep Time: 5 MINUTES • Total Time: 15 MINUTES**

# Asian Tuna Kebabs

*Remember to carefully select the salad dressing you use. Some Asian dressings have sugar in them to balance out the saltiness of the soy sauce. In this recipe, the natural sweetness of the tomatoes will serve a similar purpose.*

1 pound tuna (about 1¼" thick), cut into 16 cubes

16 cremini mushrooms

½ cup sugar-free Asian dressing

16 cherry tomatoes

8 scallions, trimmed and cut into 2" pieces

1. Soak 4 wooden skewers in water for 30 minutes.

2. Meanwhile, in a large bowl, combine the tuna, mushrooms, and dressing, tossing to coat. Let stand for 15 minutes.

3. Coat a grill or broiler rack with cooking spray. Preheat the grill or broiler. Thread 4 tuna cubes, 4 mushrooms, 4 cherry tomatoes, and 2 scallion pieces alternately onto each skewer. Grill or broil for 6 minutes, turning once, or until the tuna is opaque. Brush with the remaining dressing during the first 4 minutes of cooking.

**Serves: 4 • Prep Time: 30 MINUTES • Total Time: 40 MINUTES**

# Lime Grilled Shrimp

*If using bamboo skewers for this recipe, be sure to soak them in water for 30 minutes before threading the shrimp on them so that they don't burn.*

2 limes

4 teaspoons soy sauce

2 cloves garlic, minced

2 teaspoons grated fresh ginger

2 pounds large shrimp, peeled and deveined

1. Grate 2 teaspoons zest from the lime into a large bowl. Cut the limes in half and squeeze the juice into the bowl. Stir in the soy sauce, garlic, and ginger. Add the shrimp and toss to coat. Cover and refrigerate for 30 minutes.

2. Coat a grill rack or broiler-pan rack with cooking spray. Preheat the grill or broiler. Reserving the marinade, thread the shrimp onto 8 metal skewers, leaving ¼" between the pieces. Cook 4" from the heat for 4 minutes, turning once, or until the shrimp are opaque.

**Serves: 8 • Prep Time: 40 MINUTES • Total Time: 50 MINUTES**

# Mediterranean Shrimp and Spinach

*Ready in just 20 minutes, this tasty combination is quick enough for weeknight meals but impressive enough for company.*

1 pound large shrimp, thawed if frozen, peeled and deveined, rinsed and patted dry

3 large cloves garlic, minced and divided

2 tablespoons lemon juice

2 tablespoons extra virgin olive oil

2 tablespoons chopped fresh oregano or ½ teaspoon dried

½ teaspoon sweet paprika

¼ teaspoon freshly ground black pepper

¼ teaspoon salt

1 bag (9 ounces) baby spinach

1. On a rimmed baking sheet, place the shrimp in a mound. Drizzle with 2 minced garlic cloves, the lemon juice, 1 tablespoon of the oil, oregano or marjoram, paprika, salt, and pepper. Toss to mix. Smooth into single layer.

2. Preheat the broiler.

3. Stir the remaining 1 tablespoon oil and 1 minced garlic clove in a large nonstick skillet over medium heat. Cook, stirring, for 2 minutes, or until the garlic is fragrant. Add the spinach, in batches if necessary, tossing until wilted. Remove from the heat and cover to keep warm.

4. Broil the shrimp 4" from the heat, turning once, for 3 minutes, or until pink and just firm.

5. Transfer the spinach to a large platter and spoon the shrimp and the pan juices on top.

**Serves: 4 Prep Time: 20 minutes Total Time: 20 minutes**

# Stir-Fried Shrimp and Steamed Broccoli

*Steaming broccoli increases its content of glucosinolates, which are compounds that fight cancer. Other cooking techniques, such as frying, reduce them, according to research from Parma, Italy.*

1 pound broccoli, cut into florets

2 tablespoons water

1 tablespoon reduced-sodium soy sauce

1 clove garlic, minced

1 teaspoon minced fresh ginger

1 teaspoon red curry paste

1 pound shrimp, peeled and deveined

1 teaspoon dark sesame oil

¼ cup reduced-sodium vegetable broth

1. Place the broccoli in a large microwaveable bowl with the water. Cover loosely with plastic wrap or waxed paper and microwave on high for 3 minutes, or until tender.

2. Meanwhile, in a large bowl, whisk together the soy sauce, garlic, ginger, and curry paste. Add the shrimp and toss to coat.

3. In a large nonstick skillet over medium-high heat, heat the oil. Cook the shrimp for 3 minutes, stirring, or until opaque. Add the broth and broccoli, toss to coat, and cook for 1 minute to allow the flavors to combine.

**Serves: 4 • Prep Time: 5 MINUTES • Total Time: 15 MINUTES**

# INGREDIENT GUIDE: *Broccoli*

**TO SELECT THE BEST BROCCOLI,** look for:

- Firm stalks and firm, tightly bunched heads. Tiny yellow buds on the head signal that it is past its prime.

- Dark tops and a purplish hue indicate the presence of beta-carotene (the purple tinge will turn green when cooked).

**TO STORE,** cut a slice off the bottom of the stalk and put the head of broccoli stem side down in a large glass of water. Cover the top loosely and refrigerate for up to a week. Use this same strategy to revive a limp head of uncooked broccoli.

**TO AVOID A SULFUROUS SMELL OR TASTE,** avoid overcooking. If steaming, only partially cover the broccoli, and if boiling, don't cover it so that the natural sulfur compounds can escape. Never cook broccoli in an aluminum pan or the odor will worsen.

**TO PRESERVE THE FLAVOR** and texture of blanched broccoli, don't plunge it into a bowl of ice water. Instead, lay it on a plate or tray in a single layer and let it come to room temperature.

**TO PRESERVE NUTRIENTS,** avoid overcooking, which destroys broccoli's protective compounds. Gentle cooking helps preserve the beta-carotene. For maximum nutrient retention, lightly steam or microwave broccoli until tender-crisp.

---

**TO SERVE A WHOLE HEAD OF BROCCOLI,**
*cut off the stem so the vegetable sits at the base where its branches join together. Steam, covered, in a steamer basket over simmering water until tender in the center, about 8 minutes. Sprinkle the top with $1/2$ cup grated Cheddar or Swiss cheese, cover, and steam until the cheese melts, about 1 minute. Remove to a serving platter and carve individual servings. Makes 4 servings.*

# Italian-Style Garlic Shrimp

*If you like, you can leave the tails on the shrimp for a nice presentation. Serve with steamed broccoli. Save leftovers, if you have any, for an excellent addition to a salad.*

2 pounds large shrimp, peeled and deveined

3 tablespoons olive oil

2 tablespoons lemon juice

2 large cloves garlic, minced

1 teaspoon salt

½ teaspoon ground black pepper

2 tablespoons minced fresh parsley

1. Preheat the broiler. Line a broiler pan with foil.

2. On the prepared pan, combine the shrimp, oil, lemon juice, garlic, salt, and pepper. Toss to coat well. Arrange the shrimp in a single layer.

3. Broil for 5 minutes, turning once, or until the shrimp are opaque throughout. Transfer, with the cooking juices, to a serving platter and sprinkle with the parsley.

**Serves: 6 • Prep Time: 5 MINUTES • Total Time: 10 MINUTES**

# *Garlic and Ginger*

A relative of the onion, garlic has an assertive flavor that is an essential ingredient in many of the world's great cuisines. Keep in mind that heating garlic mellows its flavor, while chopping it intensifies the taste. Whole bulbs of roasted garlic have the mildest flavor, and raw, minced garlic has the most intense garlic taste. Also, oversize bulbs of elephant garlic have a very timid flavor that is likely to disappoint true garlic fans. Look for firm bulbs that are heavy for their size and show no signs of mold or sprouting. Keep garlic in a cool, dark place with plenty of ventilation. Avoid refrigerating garlic, which promotes rot.

Ginger is a tropical rhizome, meaning it grows from an underground stem, and is one of the essential flavors of Asian cuisine. Its pleasantly pungent flavor comes from naturally occurring chemical irritants that also create a warm sensation on the tongue. You can freeze whole, unpeeled knobs of garlic for up to 3 months in a zip-top freezer bag. Frozen ginger is much easier to grate than fresh.

# Sesame Scallops with Baby Bok Choy

*Scallops can easily become tough and chewy when overdone, so make sure you get these off the stove as soon as they are cooked through. And do take the time to dry the scallops thoroughly; it is key to getting a nice crust to form properly.*

16 sea scallops (about 1 pound)

1/4 teaspoon salt

1 egg

1/3 cup sesame seeds

1 tablespoon dark sesame oil

1 1/2 pounds baby bok choy, quartered lengthwise

1. Pat the scallops dry and sprinkle both sides with salt. In a small bowl, lightly beat the egg. Place the sesame seeds on a small plate. Dip one side of each scallop into the egg and then into the sesame seeds. Set aside.

2. In a large skillet over medium heat, heat the oil. Cook the scallops, sesame side down with space between them, for 3 to 4 minutes, or until the seeds are golden. Flip each scallop carefully without removing the sesame-seed crust. Cook for 2 minutes longer, or until opaque.

3. Meanwhile, put the bok choy into a steamer basket set over a pot of boiling water. Cover and steam for 6 minutes, or until just tender. Nestle the scallops among the bok choy quarters on each of 4 plates.

**Serves: 4 • Prep Time: 5 MINUTES • Total Time: 15 MINUTES**

# Creole-Style Steamed Clams

*When buying clams, look for those with tightly closed shells that are completely intact. They should have an appealing oceanlike scent.*

1 tablespoon olive oil

5 scallions, white parts only, finely chopped

1 small red bell pepper, finely chopped

½ rib celery, finely chopped

2 cloves garlic, minced

1 can (14.5 ounces) chopped tomatoes

¼ cup water

Pinch of ground red pepper

2 pounds littleneck or cherrystone clams, scrubbed

1. In a large pot (twice the volume of the clams) over medium heat, heat the olive oil. Cook the scallions, bell pepper, celery, and garlic for 6 minutes, stirring occasionally, or until the vegetables begin to soften. Stir in the tomatoes (with juice), water, and red pepper. Bring to a simmer.

2. Add the clams, raise the heat to medium-high, cover, and steam for 5 to 8 minutes, or until the clams open. Discard any clams that don't open. With a slotted spoon or tongs, remove the clams to serving bowls and ladle the vegetables and broth on top.

**Serves: 4 • Prep Time: 5 MINUTES • Total Time: 20 MINUTES**

# INGREDIENT GUIDE: *Apples*

**TO SELECT THE BEST APPLES,** look for:

- Firm flesh
- Smooth, tight skin that's free of blemishes and bruises
- A full and fresh scent

**TO STORE,** keep unripe apples at room temperature until they are ready to eat. Keep apples that are ready to eat in the refrigerator. To help apples last as long as possible, store them so that they aren't touching each other. Keep strong-smelling foods, such as onions, in a separate part of the fridge, because apples easily absorb odors.

**TO KEEP CUT APPLES FROM TURNING BROWN,** drop the fruit into a bowl that contains 4 cups of cold water and 4 teaspoons of lemon juice. If the sliced apples are to be baked, don't worry about them turning brown, because the browning reaction will be reversed as the apples bake.

There are over 3,000 varieties of apples, which range from mouth-puckeringly tart to candy sweet in shades of gold, pink, green, and red. Here are a few of the most popular varieties and how to use them. Note that some apples are specifically recommended for salads because they are slow to brown:

| APPLE | CHARACTERISTICS | USES |
|---|---|---|
| Cortland | Fragrant, tangy | Salads, baking, sauce, eating |
| Empire | Super-crisp, sweet, juicy | Eating, salads |
| Fuji | Sweet, juicy | Eating |
| Gala | Crisp, fragrant, mildly tart | Eating, baking, sauce |
| Golden Delicious | Juicy, sweet | Sauce, baking, salads, eating |
| Granny Smith | Tart, crisp | Baking, eating |
| McIntosh | Tart, juicy, slightly spicy, very soft | Eating, sauce |
| Winesap | Sweet, juicy, with a slightly fermented, winey flavor | Eating, sauce |

**DID YOU KNOW?** *A bruise on an apple is no different from the browning that occurs when a sliced apple is exposed to air. In both cases, compounds and enzymes in the apple's cells react with air, turning the fruit brown. Either way, the browned part is safe to eat.*

# POULTRY

# Asian Chicken Salad in Lettuce Cups

*Sriracha, a Thai sun-ripened chile sauce with garlic, adds heat and flavor to the salty-sweet peanut dip. Regular hot sauce, such as Tabasco, may be substituted.*

1 tablespoon olive oil

1 red bell pepper, cut into thin strips

½ large red onion, chopped

1½ pounds ground chicken breast

2 tablespoons chopped fresh ginger

¼ cup fresh lime juice

2 tablespoons reduced-sodium soy sauce

2 teaspoons rice wine vinegar

1 teaspoon sriracha or hot sauce, optional

½ cup chopped fresh cilantro

½ cup roasted unsalted peanuts, chopped

2 small heads Bibb lettuce, stem ends trimmed, leaves separated

1. In a large nonstick skillet over medium-high heat, warm the oil. Cook the pepper and onion for 7 minutes, stirring frequently, until lightly browned. Add the chicken and ginger and cook, crumbling the chicken as you stir, for 6 minutes, or until no longer pink. Add the lime juice, 2 tablespoons soy sauce, vinegar, and sriracha, if using. Cook for 2 minutes, or until the liquid is reduced by about half. Stir in the cilantro and the peanuts. Remove from the heat.

2. Divide the lettuce leaves and chicken mixture among 4 plates.

**Serves: 4 • Prep Time: 20 MINUTES • Total Time: 40 MINUTES**

# Chicken Stroganoff with Broccoli

*This recipe offers plenty of protein and vitamins and keeps your carbohydrate intake to a minimum.*

2 tablespoons oil

1 package (8 ounces) sliced mushrooms

1½ cups chicken broth

2 heads broccoli, cut into florets

2 cups shredded cooked chicken

¼ teaspoon salt

¼ teaspoon freshly ground black pepper

1 cup 2% plain Greek yogurt

In a large saucepan over medium-high heat, heat the oil. Cook the mushrooms for 10 minutes, or until browned. Add the broth and broccoli and bring to a simmer. Cook for 3 minutes, or until tender-crisp. Add the chicken, salt, and pepper. Cook for 5 minutes, or until the flavors blend. Remove from the heat and stir in the yogurt.

**Serves: 4 • Prep Time: 5 MINUTES • Total Time: 25 MINUTES**

# Gingered Chicken and Greens Stir-Fry

*An ideal way to use leftover greens! If you're cooking them fresh, sauté them in the same pan you'll use to stir-fry for easy cleanup.*

1 tablespoon sesame oil

1 tablespoon finely chopped fresh ginger

2 cloves garlic, thinly sliced

6 scallions, thinly sliced (keep green and white parts separate)

1 large red bell pepper, cut into thin strips

1 pound boneless, skinless chicken thighs, cut into ½" strips

¼ teaspoon salt

2 cups cooked greens (about 1 pound raw with stems)

1 tablespoon soy sauce

In a large nonstick skillet or wok over medium-high heat, heat the oil. Cook the ginger, garlic, and scallion whites for 2 minutes, stirring occasionally, or until fragrant. Add the pepper and cook for 2 minutes, or until the pepper begins to soften. Add the chicken and salt and cook for about 5 minutes, until the chicken is no longer pink in the middle. Stir in the greens, green parts of the scallions, and soy sauce.

**Serves: 4 • Prep Time: 5 MINUTES • Total Time: 15 MINUTES**

# Chicken Stir-Fry with Salsa

*Prepared salsa makes this chicken stir-fry recipe burst with flavor. Substitute any of your favorite vegetables in this versatile recipe and you'll have dinner served in less than half an hour.*

2 teaspoons olive oil

1 pound boneless, skinless chicken breasts, cut into thin strips

$\frac{1}{2}$ onion, thinly sliced

1 clove garlic, minced

$\frac{1}{2}$ red bell pepper, thinly sliced

1 cup broccoli florets

1 cup salsa

1. In a large nonstick skillet over medium heat, heat the oil. Cook the chicken, stirring frequently, for 5 minutes, or until it is no longer pink and the juices run clear. Transfer the chicken to a plate.

2. In the same skillet, cook the onion, garlic, pepper, and broccoli for 8 minutes, or until tender-crisp. Return the chicken to the skillet. Add the salsa and stir to coat. Cook for 2 minutes, or until heated through.

**Serves: 4 • Prep Time: 10 MINUTES • Total Time: 20 MINUTES**

# Chicken with Artichokes and Roasted Red Peppers

*Eating artichokes causes a chemical reaction in the mouth that stimulates the sweetness receptors on your tongue and can make other foods taste sweeter. In this particular dish, you'll likely notice the flavor of the red peppers becomes more pronounced.*

4 small boneless, skinless chicken breast halves (about 5 ounces each)

¼ teaspoon salt

¼ teaspoon freshly ground black pepper

1 tablespoon olive oil

1 red onion, cut into thin strips

1 package (10 ounces) frozen artichoke hearts, thawed

½ cup sliced jarred roasted red peppers

1 cup reduced-sodium chicken broth

1. Season the chicken with salt and pepper. In a large nonstick skillet over medium heat, heat the oil. Cook the chicken, turning once, for 12 minutes, or until a thermometer inserted in the thickest portion registers 165°F and the juices run clear. Transfer the chicken to a plate and set aside.

2. In the same skillet, cook the onion for 3 minutes. Add the artichokes, roasted peppers, and broth and bring to a boil. Cook for 3 minutes. Reduce the heat to low, add the reserved chicken, and cook for 10 minutes longer, or until heated through.

**Serves: 4 • Prep Time: 10 MINUTES • Total Time: 40 MINUTES**

# Sautéed Chicken in Rosemary-Mushroom Sauce

*Bone-in chicken breasts lend extra flavor to this dish. Of course, if you prefer boneless meats, they will work just as well.*

1 tablespoon olive oil

4 skinless chicken breast halves (bone-in)

1 large onion, halved and thinly sliced

2 cups sliced mushrooms

2 teaspoons minced garlic

1 teaspoon minced fresh rosemary

$3/4$ cup chicken broth

1 cup chopped tomatoes

2 tablespoons tomato paste

1. In a large nonstick skillet over medium-high heat, heat the oil. Cook the chicken for 5 minutes, turning once, or until browned. Transfer the chicken to a plate.

2. In the same skillet, cook the onion, mushrooms, garlic, and rosemary for 5 minutes, or until the onions are soft. Stir in the broth, tomatoes, and tomato paste. Place the chicken, bone side up, on the vegetables. Cover and cook for 30 minutes, or until a thermometer inserted in the thickest portion registers 160°F and the juices run clear.

**Serves: 4 • Prep Time: 10 MINUTES • Total Time: 50 MINUTES**

# Skillet Chicken with Spinach and Mushrooms

*This dish is very low in fat and carbs, but it's very filling and versatile. If you are not a fan of mushrooms, try substituting grilled eggplant instead.*

4 boneless, skinless chicken breast halves (about 1½ pounds), cut into 1" pieces

1 teaspoon salt

¼ teaspoon freshly ground black pepper

2 teaspoons olive oil

2 cloves garlic, minced

1 can (15 ounces) diced tomatoes, drained

1 bag (5 ounces) baby spinach

1 package (8 ounces) sliced mushrooms

½ cup grated Parmesan cheese

1. Season the chicken with salt and pepper. In a large nonstick skillet over medium heat, heat the oil. Cook the chicken for 5 to 10 minutes, or until no longer pink. Transfer the chicken to a plate, covering it to keep it warm.

2. Cook the garlic in the skillet for 2 minutes, or until the garlic is fragrant. Add the tomatoes, spinach, and mushrooms. Cook for 5 minutes, or until the liquid is reduced by half. Return the chicken to the pan and stir. Sprinkle with the cheese just before serving.

**Serves: 4 • Prep Time: 10 MINUTES • Total Time: 25 MINUTES**

# Mediterranean Chicken

*Garlic, Italian seasoning, and olives are the classic Mediterranean flavors that define this dish. Serve it with a salad or lightly roasted zucchini.*

2 tablespoons olive oil

3 cloves garlic, minced

1 teaspoon Italian seasoning

1½ pounds chicken tenders

¼ cup balsamic vinegar

2 tablespoons pitted and chopped Kalamata olives

1. Preheat the oven to 350°F. Coat a 3-quart baking dish with cooking spray.

2. In a large nonstick skillet over medium-high heat, heat the oil. Cook the garlic and Italian seasoning for 1 minute, or until fragrant. Add the chicken and cook for 3 minutes, tossing, or until lightly browned. Transfer the chicken to the prepared baking dish and top with the vinegar and olives. Bake for 20 minutes, or until the chicken is no longer pink and the juices run clear.

**Serves: 4 • Prep Time: 5 MINUTES • Total Time: 25 MINUTES**

# Grilled Jerk Chicken

*Allspice is an extremely versatile spice that lives up to its name. It has hints of cinnamon, clove, and nutmeg, all rolled into one perfectly balanced flavor.*

4 cloves garlic, minced

¼ cup white wine vinegar

1½ tablespoons olive oil

1 tablespoon minced fresh ginger

1 tablespoon ground allspice

½ teaspoon salt

½ teaspoon ground black pepper

4 small boneless, skinless chicken breast halves (5 ounces each)

1. In a large bowl, combine the garlic, vinegar, oil, ginger, allspice, salt, and pepper. Add the chicken and turn to coat on all sides. Cover and refrigerate for just 1 hour.

2. Preheat the grill to medium. Grill the chicken, turning once, for 10 to 15 minutes, or until cooked through and a thermometer inserted into the thickest portion registers 165°F.

**Serves: 4 • Prep Time: 5 MINUTES • Total Time: 20 MINUTES + MARINATING TIME**

# Chicken Piccata

*Here's a simple way to prepare classic piccata without using wheat flour and all the fat.*

1 pound chicken cutlets

¼ teaspoon salt

¼ teaspoon pepper

¼ cup extra-virgin olive oil

½ cup chicken broth

1 medium shallot, minced, or 1 large clove garlic, minced

1 lemon, ½ thinly sliced and ½ juiced

2 tablespoons capers

2 tablespoons chopped fresh parsley

1. Sprinkle the chicken with the salt and pepper.

2. In a large skillet over medium heat, warm the oil. Working in batches, if necessary, cook the chicken for 6 minutes, turning once, or until golden brown, no longer pink, and the juices run clear. Transfer to a warm platter and cover loosely with foil.

3. Add the broth, shallot or garlic, and lemon slices to the skillet, increase the heat to high, and cook, stirring to loosen any browned bits. Boil for 4 minutes, or until the broth has reduced by half. Add the lemon juice and capers and continue simmering for 2 minutes. Stir in the parsley. Spoon the sauce over the chicken.

**Serves: 4 • Prep Time: 5 MINUTES • Total Time: 25 MINUTES**

# INGREDIENT GUIDE: *Grapes*

**TO SELECT THE BEST GRAPES,** look for:

- Full, plump clusters with no bruises or soft spots
- Green and pliable stems, an indicator of freshness

**TO STORE,** refrigerate grapes in a loosely closed plastic bag. Many varieties of grapes have a white powder coating known as bloom, which helps keep grapes moist. Avoid washing off the bloom until just before serving or using.

**TO MAINTAIN FRESHNESS,** check grapes every day or two for signs of spoiling while storing. Just a little bit of mold can infect and spread through a whole bunch of grapes. Discard any fruit that shows signs of spoilage.

**TO FREEZE,** lay individual grapes in a single layer on a baking sheet and freeze until solid. Then transfer to plastic bags or an airtight container in the freezer. The high sugar content in grapes keeps them from freezing solid. They'll last as long as a month in the freezer, and they make a cool treat on a hot summer day.

**TO SERVE GRAPES,** you'll enjoy a most pronounced flavor in your grapes if you bring them to room temperature.

**DID YOU KNOW?** There are thousands of varieties of grapes. Some are grown for snacking, others for making wine, and there are also special varieties for raisins, grape juice, and jelly.

---

**FASCINATING FACT:** *The word* grape *comes from the name of the tool used long ago to "grapple" this fruit from the vines.*

# Lime-Marinated Chicken with Fresh Salsa

*Never eat dry chicken breasts again! If you've been overcooking chicken because you're not certain when it's done, use an instant-read digital thermometer to gauge the internal temperature. Your poultry will be moist every time.*

4 small boneless, skinless chicken breasts (about 5 ounces each)

3 tablespoons lime juice

2 tablespoons olive oil

1¼ teaspoons ground cumin

¼ teaspoon salt

3 medium tomatoes, chopped

½ avocado, peeled, pitted, and chopped

½ small red onion, chopped (optional)

½ cup chopped fresh cilantro

1. Place the chicken in a large resealable plastic bag. In a medium bowl, whisk together the lime juice, oil, cumin, and salt. Spoon 3 tablespoons of the mixture over the chicken and squeeze the bag to coat. Chill the chicken for 1 hour. Add the tomatoes, avocado, onion (if using), and cilantro to the bowl with the reserved marinade. Set aside.

2. Coat a grill rack or broiler pan with cooking spray. Preheat the grill or broiler. Grill or broil the chicken, 4" from the heat source, for 10 minutes, turning once, or until a thermometer inserted into the thickest portion registers 165°F and the juices run clear.

3. To serve, evenly divide the chicken and salsa among 4 plates.

**Serves: 4 • Prep Time: 15 MINUTES • Total Time: 25 MINUTES + MARINATING TIME**

# Chicken Roll-Up with Spinach and Sun-Dried Tomatoes

*Before pounding the cutlets, try sandwiching the poultry between two sheets of parchment paper. It will help minimize cross-contamination and keep the poultry from tearing.*

2 cups baby spinach

2 tablespoons olive oil, divided

1 small onion, finely chopped

1 clove garlic, minced

¼ cup (1 ounce) grated Parmesan cheese

4 chicken cutlets (about 4 ounces each) or chicken breast halves, trimmed and pounded thin into cutlets

2 tablespoons chopped dry-packed sun-dried tomatoes

½ cup chicken broth

1. In a large ovenproof nonstick skillet over medium heat, cook the spinach with a tablespoon or two of water, covered, for 2 minutes, tossing occasionally, or until wilted. Drain and press firmly with the back of a spoon or squeeze to remove excess moisture. Wipe out the skillet. Transfer the spinach to a medium bowl.

2. In the same skillet over medium heat, heat 1 tablespoon of the oil. Cook the onion and garlic for 5 minutes, or until softened. Transfer to the bowl with the spinach. Stir the cheese into the bowl.

3. Place the chicken on a work surface. Sprinkle the tomatoes evenly on the smooth side of the chicken. Divide the spinach mixture among the cutlets. Spread to the edges of 3 sides, leaving about 1" at the narrow tip free of spinach mixture. Loosely roll up the chicken, ending with the narrow tip, and secure with wooden picks.

4. In the same skillet over medium heat, warm the remaining 1 tablespoon of oil and cook the chicken for about 10 minutes, turning occasionally, or until golden brown on all sides. Add the broth, cover, and cook over low heat for 7 minutes, or until no longer pink and the juices run clear. Transfer to a warm platter and cover loosely with foil.

5. Boil the skillet juices for 5 minutes, or until reduced to a glaze. Slice the chicken diagonally into 1"-thick pieces. Drizzle with the pan juices before serving.

**Serves: 4 • Prep Time: 10 MINUTES • Total Time: 40 MINUTES**

Poultry

# Lemon-Basil Chicken

*Tucking fresh herbs under the skin of chicken breasts adds an amazing amount of flavor. Serve with broccoli rabe that has been cooked in olive oil with garlic and red pepper flakes.*

4 bone-in, skin-on chicken breast halves

8 fresh basil leaves plus ¼ cup chopped fresh basil

2 tablespoons olive oil, divided

½ teaspoon salt, divided

¼ teaspoon ground black pepper

1 lemon, cut crosswise into 4 to 8 slices

1 tablespoon red wine vinegar

1½ teaspoons Dijon mustard

2 large tomatoes, chopped

1. Preheat the oven to 400°F. Coat a 13" x 9" baking pan with cooking spray. With your fingers, carefully loosen the skin from the breast of the chicken. Tuck 2 basil leaves under the skin of each breast. Place the chicken in the baking dish. Drizzle with 1 tablespoon of the oil and sprinkle with ¼ teaspoon of the salt and the pepper. Place the lemon slices over the chicken.

2. Bake for 35 minutes, basting occasionally with the pan juices, or until a thermometer inserted in the thickest portion (not touching the bone) registers 170°F.

3. Meanwhile, in a medium bowl, whisk together the vinegar, mustard, the remaining 1 tablespoon oil, and remaining ¼ teaspoon salt. Stir in the tomatoes and chopped basil and toss to coat well. Divide the tomato mixture among 4 plates and top with the chicken.

**Serves: 4 • Prep Time: 15 MINUTES • Total Time: 50 MINUTES**

# Curried Chicken and Broccoli Casserole

*It's a cinch to assemble this oven-baked dinner up to a day ahead of cooking. Simply cool the broccoli before putting all the ingredients together. Cover with plastic wrap and refrigerate until baking time.*

1 pound broccoli florets

¼ cup mayonnaise

1 tablespoon lemon juice

1½ teaspoons curry powder

½ teaspoon salt

½ teaspoon ground black pepper

1½ pounds boneless, skinless chicken breasts, cut into bite-size chunks

¼ cup shredded reduced-fat Colby or Swiss cheese

1. Preheat the oven to 350°F. Coat a 13" x 9" baking dish with cooking spray. Place the broccoli in a large microwaveable bowl with a few tablespoons of water. Cover loosely with plastic wrap or waxed paper and microwave on high for 3 to 4 minutes, or until tender-crisp. Drain and set aside.

2. In a small bowl, stir together the mayonnaise, lemon juice, curry powder, salt, and pepper. Line the prepared baking dish with the reserved broccoli. Top with the chicken. Drizzle with the mayonnaise mixture. Sprinkle with the cheese. Cover and bake for 25 minutes. Uncover and bake for 15 minutes longer, or until golden and bubbling.

**Serves: 6 • Prep Time: 10 MINUTES • Total Time: 1 HOUR**

# Delicious Dill Chicken

*This is a tasty, family-friendly dish that is sure to draw rave reviews. Serve leftovers over greens for a delicious salad.*

2 tablespoons minced fresh dill

2 tablespoons Worcestershire sauce

1/2 teaspoon soy sauce

1 small onion, finely chopped

1/4 teaspoon salt

1/4 teaspoon ground black pepper

4 small boneless, skinless chicken breast halves (about 5 ounces each)

1. In a resealable plastic bag, combine the dill, Worcestershire sauce, soy sauce, onion, salt, and pepper. Add the chicken and gently massage the ingredients in the closed bag. Chill for at least 30 minutes, preferably overnight.

2. Preheat the oven to 350°F. Coat a 9" x 9" baking dish with cooking spray. Place the chicken and marinade in the prepared pan. Bake for 25 minutes, or until a thermometer inserted into the thickest part of the chicken registers 165°F and the juices run clear.

**Serves: 4 • Prep Time: 5 MINUTES • Total Time: 30 MINUTES + MARINATING TIME**

# Turkey Cutlets with Oregano-Lemon Sauce

*Turkey isn't just for Thanksgiving anymore! Serve these cutlets on a bed of grilled asparagus or sautéed baby kale.*

1 pound turkey breast cutlets

¾ teaspoon dried oregano, divided

½ teaspoon salt

1 tablespoon olive oil

2 cloves garlic, minced

¼ cup reduced-sodium chicken broth

3 tablespoons fresh lemon juice

1. Sprinkle the turkey with ½ teaspoon of the oregano and the salt.

2. In a large nonstick skillet over medium-high heat, heat the oil. Working in batches, cook the turkey for 6 minutes, turning once, or until golden and no longer pink. Transfer to a warm platter and cover loosely with foil.

3. Add the garlic to the skillet and cook for 1 minute, or until fragrant. Add the broth, lemon juice, and the remaining ¼ teaspoon oregano. Cook, stirring, for 2 to 3 minutes, or until hot. Pour the sauce over the turkey.

**Serves: 4 • Prep Time: 5 MINUTES • Total Time: 15 MINUTES**

# INGREDIENT GUIDE: *Oranges*

**TO SELECT THE BEST ORANGES,** look for:

- Fruit that feels heavy for its size

- An absence of mold or soft spots

- Characteristics beyond color (some oranges are dyed with food coloring)

**THERE ARE THREE MAIN CATEGORIES OF ORANGES:** sweet oranges, mandarin oranges, and sour oranges. Sweet oranges, which are usually large, sweet, and juicy, include navel oranges (popular for eating out of hand because most are seedless), Valencia oranges (extremely juicy), and blood oranges (prized for their red flesh). Mandarin oranges include tangerines, clementines, tangelos, and honey oranges. These varieties all have thin, loose skins and range in flavor from sweet to slightly tart. Sour, or bitter, oranges are usually used to make marmalade and liqueurs and require a good amount of sugar to balance their strong flavors, so they're not recommended as part of the Lose It Now, Lose It Forever eating plan.

**TO STORE,** keep oranges in a cold, dry place for a few days or refrigerate for up to 2 weeks.

**TO ZEST AN ORANGE** and remove the flavorful outer edge of skin, use a citrus zester, a grater, or a vegetable peeler. Avoid taking the bitter white pith beneath the outer orange zest. Be sure to zest oranges before juicing them; it's nearly impossible to remove the zest once they've been juiced.

**TO MAKE ORANGE "SUPREMES"** and enjoy segments that are free of their protective outer membrane, begin by slicing off about ½" from the top (stem end) and bottom of a large, firm navel orange. Remove the zest and white pith as you cut. Stand the orange on end and cut downward all around, cutting just beneath the white pith to remove the entire rind in strips. Stand the rindless orange on end (or in your hand) and remove one orange segment at a time by running the knife close to the membrane, releasing each segment. Squeeze the remaining accordion-like membrane over the supremes to extract any juice.

---

**DID YOU KNOW?** *Oranges are native to southern China and southeast Asia. They have been cultivated for approximately 4,000 years.*

# MEAT

# Stuffed Lamb Chops

*Prized for its tenderness and delicate flavor, lamb pairs especially well with spinach and thyme. Serve with the Sautéed Cherry Tomatoes with White Beans on page 47.*

1½ cups fresh spinach

1 tablespoon pine nuts

¼ teaspoon dried thyme

¼ teaspoon salt

¼ teaspoon ground black pepper

4 loin lamb chops (about 4 ounces each)

1 teaspoon olive oil

2 tablespoons red wine or balsamic vinegar

1. In a small skillet over low heat, cook the spinach and pine nuts for 3 minutes, or until the spinach is bright green and wilted. Remove from the heat and stir in the thyme, salt, and pepper. Let cool.

2. Cut a small pocket into the side of each lamb chop and stuff with equal amounts of the spinach mixture. In a large skillet over medium heat, heat the oil. Cook the stuffed lamb chops for 8 minutes, turning once. Add the vinegar and cook for 2 minutes, or until most of the liquid has evaporated. The chops should be browned, and a thermometer inserted in the center should register 145°F for medium-rare.

**Serves: 4 • Prep Time: 10 MINUTES • Total Time: 20 MINUTES**

# Thai Beef Lettuce Wraps

*Lettuce wraps make a great fun meal because everyone gets to assemble their creations just as they would like them.*

12 ounces flank, skirt, or sirloin steak

    Salt and ground black pepper to taste

2 tablespoons fish sauce or soy sauce

1 tablespoon Sriracha or Tabasco hot sauce

1 lime, juiced

1 head Bibb lettuce, washed and dried, leaves separated

1 jalapeño pepper, thinly sliced

½ red onion, thinly sliced

½ cup chopped fresh cilantro

1 cup bean sprouts

1. Heat a grill or grill pan over high heat for at least 5 minutes. Season the steak with salt and pepper and cook for 8 minutes, turning once, or until a thermometer inserted in the center registers 145°F for medium-rare. Let it rest for 5 minutes.

2. Meanwhile, in a small saucepan, combine the fish or soy sauce, hot sauce, and lime juice. Cook over low heat for 5 minutes, or until hot and the flavors blend. Slice the steak thinly (if it's skirt or flank steak, be sure to cut against the grain) and drizzle half of the warm sauce over it.

3. Divide the lettuce between 2 plates. Fill each with half the steak, the jalapeño slices, onion slices, cilantro, bean sprouts, and remaining sauce. Use the leaves like tortillas to wrap up the steak slices with the other ingredients.

**Serves: 2 • Prep Time: 10 MINUTES • Total Time: 25 MINUTES**

# INGREDIENT GUIDE: *Greens*

**TO SELECT THE BEST GREENS,** look for:

- Vibrant, brightly colored leaves, which are an indication of freshness

- Cook greens during the cool months of fall, winter, and early spring. (Generally, they don't tolerate heat well and can become more bitter in the summer months.)

**TO STORE,** cover greens with a perforated plastic bag and store in the refrigerator. Clean just before using.

**TO WASH,** cut and discard the hard ends from the stems. Slice the stems into ¼" to ½" pieces. Toss together in a large bowl and cover with cold water. Swoosh the greens in the water vigorously to rid them of sand and dirt. Lift the greens from the water, leaving the dirt in the bottom of the bowl. Do not pour into a colander or a strainer to drain, which will throw the dirt back into the leaves.

**TO COOK TENDER GREENS,** such as spinach, beets, dandelion, or watercress, trim and wash 1 to 1½ pounds, leaving them slightly wet. Heat 2 teaspoons olive oil in a large heavy skillet. Add the wet greens along with a big pinch of salt, a small pinch of red pepper flakes, and a minced garlic clove. Cover and cook until tender, anywhere from 1 minute for baby spinach to 7 minutes for turnip greens. Remove the cover and boil off any remaining liquid.

**TO COOK TOUGH GREENS,** such as kale, collards, and broccoli rabe, you'll need to plan on a slightly longer cooking time to soften their leaves and tame any aggressive flavors. Simmer in a few cups of water or broth in a covered pan until soft, about 5 to 25 minutes, depending upon the toughness of the green.

---

**TO GET MAXIMUM NUTRIENTS,** *cut the tougher greens, such as kale and Swiss chard, into strips and cook them in boiling water. This will allow them to cook quickly to a tender state, preserving the maximum amount of nutrition.*

# Custom Spice Mixes

Buying premixed spices at the grocery can be far more expensive than making your own custom blend from ingredients you already have on hand. Plus, you can adjust for heat or sweetness according to your preference. Try one of these the next time you decide to grill. Rub any of the following seasoning blends into beef, pork, lamb, or chicken. Each makes enough for 1 to 2 pounds of meat. Wrap the meat in plastic and refrigerate for several hours before cooking.

**CAROLINA SPICE RUB:** Combine 2 tablespoons paprika, 2 teaspoons brown sugar, and ½ teaspoon each of celery salt, ground black pepper, dry mustard, and onion powder. Makes ¼ cup.

**TROPICAL SPICE RUB:** Combine 2 teaspoons each of dried cilantro, garlic powder, and salt, and 1 teaspoon each of ground black pepper, ground cumin, and ground oregano. Makes 3 tablespoons.

**MIDEAST SPICE RUB:** Combine 2 teaspoons ground black pepper, 1½ teaspoons ground cumin, 1 teaspoon each of ground coriander and salt, ½ teaspoon ground cardamom, and ¼ teaspoon ground cloves. Makes about 2 tablespoons.

# Cowboy Flank Steak

*Add flavor without fat, carbs, or calories with a spice rub. For even more intense flavors, the steak may be rubbed with the spice mixture and refrigerated up to 1 day ahead.*

2 teaspoons ground cumin

2 teaspoons smoked paprika

1 teaspoon chili powder

1/2 teaspoon garlic powder

1/2 teaspoon onion powder

1/2 teaspoon salt

1 beef flank steak or top round steak (1¼ pounds), trimmed of all visible fat

1. In a small bowl, combine the cumin, paprika, chili powder, garlic powder, onion powder, and salt.

2. Lightly oil a grill rack or broiler-pan rack. Preheat the grill or broiler. Place the steak on the prepared rack and rub the cumin mixture over both sides of the steak. Let stand at room temperature for 30 minutes or cover and chill for up to 24 hours.

3. Grill or broil the steak for 8 minutes, turning once, or until a thermometer inserted in the center registers 145°F for medium-rare. Place the steak on a cutting board and let stand for 5 minutes. Cut the steak into thin slices.

**Serves: 6 • Prep Time: 5 MINUTES • Total Time: 20 MINUTES + MARINATING TIME**

## *Chili Powder*

Commercial chili powder is a blend of various ground, dried chile peppers and seasonings such as garlic and onion powder. It is fine for most purposes, but for deeper flavor use pure chile powder made from ground dried chile peppers. If you've run out of chili powder, here's a quick mix to get you by: 1 tablespoon ground cumin, 1 teaspoon each dried oregano, garlic powder, and onion powder, ½ teaspoon each ground red pepper and paprika, and ¼ teaspoon ground allspice. This makes about 2½ tablespoons.

Meat

# Grilled Steak with Peppers

*Steamed broccolini, broccoli, or cauliflower with a squeeze of fresh lemon juice makes a great side dish for this hearty meal.*

2 tablespoons olive oil

1 large onion, sliced

2 large red bell peppers, sliced

2 large yellow bell peppers, sliced

1 clove garlic, minced

1 tablespoon minced fresh or
½ teaspoon dried oregano

½ teaspoon salt

1 tablespoon balsamic vinegar

1 tablespoon capers, rinsed (optional)

1½ pounds flank steak

Fresh oregano leaves for garnish
(optional)

1. In a large skillet over medium heat, heat the oil. Cook the onion and peppers for 10 minutes, stirring occasionally, until tender and lightly browned. Add the garlic, oregano, and salt and cook for 1 minute. Stir in the vinegar and capers (if using) and cook for 2 minutes, stirring to loosen any brown bits.

2. Coat a grill rack with cooking spray. Heat the grill to medium-high. Grill the steak for 10 minutes, turning once, or until a thermometer inserted in the center registers 145°F for medium-rare. Place the steak on a cutting board and let stand for 5 minutes. Cut the steak into thin slices. Top with the pepper sauce and oregano leaves, if desired.

**Serves: 4 • Prep Time: 10 MINUTES • Total Time: 35 MINUTES**

# Flatiron Steak with Balsamic-Mustard Sauce

*A flatiron steak is a rectangular piece of meat cut from the shoulder that makes an especially nice special-occasion meal. Sirloin steak is a good substitute if you can't find flatirons at your grocery.*

4 flatiron steaks (6 to 8 ounces each)

¼ teaspoon salt

¼ teaspoon freshly ground black pepper

1 tablespoon olive oil

¼ cup balsamic vinegar

¾ cup chicken broth

1 teaspoon Dijon mustard

1 tablespoon unsalted butter

1. Season the steaks with the salt and pepper. In a large skillet over medium-high heat, heat the oil. Cook the steaks for about 3 minutes per side, or until a thermometer inserted in the center registers 145°F for medium-rare. Remove from the skillet, cover with foil, and keep warm while you make the sauce.

2. Add the vinegar to the skillet and cook for about 30 seconds, scraping up any browned bits that cling to the bottom of the pan. Add the broth and mustard and cook until slightly thickened, about 3 minutes. Add the butter and swirl the pan until the butter has melted. Serve the steaks with the sauce spooned on top.

**Serves: 4 • Prep Time: 5 MINUTES • Total Time: 15 MINUTES**

# INGREDIENT GUIDE: *Cheese*

**TO SELECT THE BEST CHEESE,** look for:

- A market that takes pride in its cheeses and allows you to taste before you buy

- Cheese without cracks, discoloration, or signs of mold (unless buying blue cheese)

**TO STORE,** wrap cheese tightly in plastic wrap, aluminum foil, or waxed paper and keep it in the cheese drawer of your refrigerator or another not-too-cold spot. Once you've unwrapped the cheese, always discard the wrapping and rewrap in fresh wrapping. In general, the harder the cheese, the longer it will stay fresh.

**TO SERVE:** Always bring ripened cheese to room temperature before serving. Cold cheese right out of the refrigerator will never have the full, rich flavor of cheese at room temperature.

**TO GRATE CHEESE QUICKLY,** coat the grater lightly with oil. This will prevent the cheese from sticking and make for easier cleanup.

**TO CUT CHEESE,** all you really need is a good sharp knife, preferably one with a thin blade. To cut soft or semisoft cheeses, such as a goat cheese, slice through with a tautly pulled piece of dental floss.

**TO QUICKLY SLICE MOZZARELLA,** use an egg slicer. Place a ball of mozzarella in the cradle of the slicer and slice with the wires. For julienned pieces, turn the sliced cheese 90 degrees and slice again.

---

**TO KEEP MOZZARELLA FROM GETTING STRINGY WHEN COOKED,** *add an acid, such as lemon juice, to the dish.*

# Filet of Beef with Grilled Onions

*Filet mignon is an exceptionally lean and tender cut of beef that's often wrapped in bacon, which dramatically undercuts its nutritional benefits. Fortunately, this king of cuts is equally regal enrobed in sweet onions and spices alongside cooked spinach.*

| | |
|---|---|
| 1 teaspoon garlic powder | ⅛ teaspoon ground black pepper |
| ½ teaspoon salt | 4 pieces filet mignon (4 ounces each) |
| ¼ teaspoon ground red pepper | 2 cups sliced Vidalia onions |

1. Mix the garlic powder, salt, and red and black pepper. Sprinkle this mixture over each side of the filets and set aside.

2. Coat a grill rack with cooking spray and heat the grill to medium heat. Cook the onions for 10 minutes, stirring occasionally, until lightly browned. Transfer the onions to a plate and cover to keep warm.

3. Increase the heat up to high. Grill the meat for 8 minutes, turning once, or until a thermometer inserted in the center registers 145°F for medium-rare. Serve the onions on the steak.

**Serves: 4 • Prep Time: 5 MINUTES • Total Time: 25 MINUTES**

# Beef-Vegetable Kebabs

*These kebabs can be assembled a few hours before cooking. If you use wooden skewers, be sure to soak them in water for 30 minutes before using.*

1 pound top sirloin steak or sirloin steak, cut into 1½" cubes

1 red bell pepper, cut into 12 pieces

1 yellow bell pepper, cut into 12 pieces

1 small eggplant, cut into 12 cubes

1 red onion, cut into 12 chunks

⅓ cup sugar-free Italian seasoning

1. In a large resealable plastic bag, combine the beef, red pepper, yellow pepper, eggplant, and onion. Seal it and toss to coat the vegetables with the marinade. Chill for at least 1 hour, turning the bag over occasionally.

2. Coat a grill rack with cooking spray and preheat the grill to medium-high. Assemble the kebabs on four 12" metal skewers or eight 6" wooden skewers, threading a few vegetables in between pieces of beef. Don't overcrowd the skewers.

3. Grill for 8 minutes for medium-rare, turning occasionally, or until desired doneness.

**Serves: 4 • Prep Time: 15 MINUTES • Total Time: 25 MINUTES + MARINATING TIME**

Meat

# Zesty Beef Kebabs

*These kebabs are a great meal for company. Prepare the meat and vegetables ahead of time and refrigerate until just before serving. Let your guests help thread the meat and vegetables onto the skewers before cooking.*

1 tablespoon balsamic vinegar

1 tablespoon olive oil

1 tablespoon horseradish

½ teaspoon dried thyme

1 clove garlic, minced

1 pound lean boneless sirloin, trimmed and cut into 1" pieces

1 sweet onion, such as Vidalia, cut into 16 pieces

1 green bell pepper, cut into 16 pieces

12 cherry tomatoes

½ teaspoon salt

1. In a large bowl, whisk together the vinegar, oil, horseradish, thyme, and garlic. Add the beef and toss to coat. Cover and refrigerate for 2 hours or overnight.

2. Preheat the broiler and coat a broiler-pan rack with cooking spray. Alternately thread 5 beef cubes, 4 onion pieces, 4 bell pepper squares, and 3 cherry tomatoes onto each of four 18" metal skewers. Place the skewers onto the broiler pan and sprinkle with the salt. Broil 4" from the heat source for 8 minutes, turning occasionally, until the vegetables are tender and the beef is cooked through.

**Serves: 4 • Prep Time: 20 MINUTES • Total Time: 20 MINUTES + MARINATING TIME**

# *Horseradish*

Horseradish is a distinct seasoning that works well with beef, smoked fish, and strong-flavored vegetables. Interestingly, horseradish has virtually no aroma until you scratch its skin; then, it will emit a sharp, penetrating aroma that will likely clear your sinuses. To use fresh horseradish, peel the root and remove the fibrous core before grating (the shredding blade of a food processor comes in handy for chores like this). Use or freeze grated horseradish immediately, as its flavor tends to fade quickly. If buying prepared horseradish, steer clear of any jars with purple-red contents; the horseradish has been packed with grated beetroot.

# Peppercorn Pork with Roasted Vegetables

*Anytime you want to dress up this dish for company, replace the zucchini with baby squash and the regular cherry tomatoes with yellow ones.*

2 teaspoons peppercorns

2 pounds pork tenderloin

2 pints cherry or grape tomatoes

2 small zucchini, cut into chunks

2 tablespoons olive oil

½ teaspoon salt

½ teaspoon freshly ground black pepper

½ cup slivered fresh basil leaves (optional)

1. Preheat the oven to 375°F. Coat a 17" x 11" baking pan or other large shallow baking pan with cooking spray. Crush the peppercorns with the flat side of a chef's knife or with the bottom of a heavy skillet. Rub the peppercorns into the pork and set aside.

2. Place the tomatoes, zucchini, oil, salt, and pepper in the pan. Stir to coat the tomatoes and zucchini. Pushing the tomatoes and zucchini aside, place the pork in the center of the pan and arrange it so that it doesn't touch the edges of the pan or the other foods. Roast for 45 minutes, or until a thermometer inserted into the center registers 145°F and the juices run clear. Let stand 10 minutes and then cut the pork into thin slices. Serve with the tomatoes and zucchini, sprinkled with the basil, if using.

**Serves: 6 • Prep Time: 10 MINUTES • Total Time: 1 HOUR 10 MINUTES**

# Quick Pork Chops with Green Salsa

*Looking a bit like green tomatoes wrapped in parchment, tomatillos have a bright lemony flavor that adds a distinct twist to salsas. When purchasing, look for firm, unblemished tomatillos that completely fill their husks. They will keep well, refrigerated, for up to 3 weeks.*

4 boneless pork chops (3 ounces each), trimmed of all visible fat

1 teaspoon ground cumin

¼ teaspoon salt

3 teaspoons olive oil, divided

6 tomatillos, cut into wedges

4 scallions, cut into ½" pieces

1 clove garlic, minced

½ cup fat-free, reduced-sodium chicken broth

¼ cup chopped fresh cilantro

1. Rub the chops with the cumin and salt. In a large nonstick skillet over medium-high heat, heat 2 teaspoons of the oil. Cook the chops for 5 minutes, turning once, or until a thermometer inserted in the center of a chop registers 145°F and the juices run clear. Remove to a plate and keep warm.

2. Heat the remaining teaspoon of oil in the same skillet over medium-high heat. Cook the tomatillos, scallions, and garlic, stirring constantly, for 5 minutes, or until browned. Add the broth and cilantro and cook for 3 minutes, or until the flavors meld. Serve with the chops.

**Serves: 4 • Prep Time: 15 MINUTES • Total Time: 30 MINUTES**

# Sunday Pork Roast

*Prep this roast early in the morning and dinner will be ready when you are. Serve with roasted vegetables and mashed cauliflower for an old-time family dinner.*

¼ cup tomato sauce

1 tablespoon balsamic vinegar

1 small onion, minced

1 clove garlic, minced

½ teaspoon salt

½ teaspoon ground black pepper

1 boneless pork roast (2¾ to 3 pounds), trimmed of fat

1. In a small bowl, combine the tomato sauce, vinegar, onion, garlic, salt, and pepper.

2. Place the pork roast in a slow cooker. Pour the tomato mixture over the roast. Cover and cook on low for 6 to 8 hours, or until tender and no longer pink.

**Serves: 8 • Prep Time: 5 MINUTES • Total Time: 6 HOURS 5 MINUTES**

# 7-DAY MEAL PLANS

*E*ating the Lose It Now way is delicious and simple when you prepare the recipes featured in this cookbook. Following are 7 days of sample meal plans to show just how easy and tasty it can be to Lose It Now, Lose It Forever.

In the Lose It Now, Lose It Forever book, see page 134 to include carbs into these meals for Phase 2.

### DAY 1

*Breakfast*

**Broccoli-Cheddar Scramble (page 5)**

Reduced-sodium vegetable juice, coffee, or tea

*Midmorning*

1 serving fresh berries (fist-size portion, about ½ cup)

*Lunch*

**Tuna and Chickpea Salad in Tomato Cups (page 62)**

Unsweetened iced tea or sparkling water

*Midafternoon*

1 serving walnuts (small handful)

*Dinner*

**Gingered Chicken and Greens Stir-Fry (page 95)**

Unsweetened iced tea or sparkling water

## DAY 2

### *Breakfast*

**Easy Veggie Omelet (page 7)**

Reduced-sodium vegetable juice, coffee, or tea

### *Midmorning*

1 small apple

### *Lunch*

Broiled shrimp

Steamed broccoli

Unsweetened iced tea or sparkling water

### *Midafternoon*

1 serving almonds (small handful)

### *Dinner*

Roasted chicken

**Asparagus with Tomato Vinaigrette (page 40)**

Unsweetened iced tea or sparkling water

## *Breakfast*

**Frittata with Smoked Salmon and Scallions (page 11)**

Reduced-sodium vegetable juice, coffee, or tea

## *Midmorning*

1 small orange

## *Lunch*

Grilled hamburger (no roll) with lettuce, tomato, and onion slices

Steamed broccoli and cauliflower

Unsweetened iced tea or sparkling water

## *Midafternoon*

1 serving walnuts (small handful)

## *Dinner*

**Spicy Fish with Peppers (page 75)**

**Curried Roasted Cauliflower with Flaxseeds (page 43)**

Unsweetened iced tea or sparkling water

## Breakfast

**Spinach-Tomato Frittata (page 15)**

Coffee or tea

## Midmorning

1 portion grapes (fist-size portion, about ½ cup)

## Lunch

Green leaf lettuce with bell pepper, celery, roasted chicken, and a drizzle of oil and vinegar

Unsweetened iced tea or sparkling water

## Midafternoon

1 serving almonds (small handful)

## Dinner

**Cowboy Flank Steak (page 123)**

Grilled zucchini

Unsweetened iced tea or sparkling water

## Breakfast

**Deviled Eggs (page 6)**

Reduced-sodium vegetable juice, coffee, or tea

## Midmorning

1 portion berries (fist-size portion, about ½ cup)

## Lunch

**Tuna Salad in Lettuce Wrappers (page 61)**

Unsweetened iced tea or sparkling water

## Midafternoon

1 serving pistachios (small handful)

## Dinner

Grilled pork tenderloin

**Grilled Eggplant (page 49)\***

Green salad

Unsweetened iced tea or sparkling water

*\*Save leftovers for another side dish in a few days.*

## Breakfast

**Green Eggs and Ham Cups (page 17)\***

Reduced-sodium vegetable juice, coffee, or tea

## Midmorning

1 small apple

## Lunch

**Salmon Salad in Lettuce Cups (page 65)**

Unsweetened iced tea or sparkling water

## Midafternoon

1 serving walnuts (small handful)

## Dinner

Roasted cod or salmon

Green salad

Steamed cauliflower

Unsweetened iced tea or sparkling water

*\*Save leftovers for another breakfast in a few days.*

## Breakfast

**Sausage, Egg, and Vegetable Casserole (page 20)***

Reduced-sodium vegetable juice, coffee, or tea

## Midmorning

1 small orange

## Lunch

**Butternut Squash Soup (page 26)**

Salad with your favorite low-GI vegetables and turkey breast

Unsweetened iced tea or sparkling water

## Midafternoon

1 serving almonds (small handful)

## Dinner

**Sautéed Chicken in Rosemary-Mushroom Sauce (page 99)**

Sautéed broccoli rabe

Unsweetened iced tea or sparkling water

*Save leftovers for another breakfast in a few days.*

# INDEX

Boldface page numbers indicate photographs. <u>Underscored</u> references indicate boxed text.